IDENTIFICATION OF THE BRITISH MOLLUSCA

D1628365

Hulton Group Keys

IDENTIFICATION OF THE BRITISH MOLLUSCA

by
GORDON E. BEEDHAM, B.Sc., Ph.D.
Head of Department of Biological Science
North East London Polytechnic

Editor of series: **Antony R. Kenney, M.A., B.Sc.**

©
1972
G. E. Beedham
A. R. Kenney

ISBN 0 7175 0593 6

First published 1972 by Hulton Educational Publications Ltd., Raans Road, Amersham, Bucks.
Printed in Great Britain at the Pitman Press, Bath.

PREFACE

This book is not intended to be the definitive guide to all the British Mollusca. Indeed, with 800 or so species living in a wide range of marine, freshwater and terrestrial environments, a complete survey of the whole molluscan fauna of the British Isles is outside the scope of any relatively small compendium. However, it is claimed that the present volume introduces the beginner to a representative selection both of the commoner British molluscs and of those species which, although less frequently found, are of especial interest in understanding the great variety of form and habitat which so characterise the molluscan way of life. Diagnostic characters, habitat and general features of interest of some 215 of the better known species are summarised, many more are briefly described and 282 molluscs are individually illustrated, with some characteristic shells photographed in colour. The text is kept as non-technical as possible and the intention throughout is to guide the keen newcomer through the major molluscan groups via their most typical representatives, and to tempt him to delve further into those particular assemblages which come to interest him most. Ability to recognise a wide range of the commoner species is often a necessary first step in identification which will then enable the collector to embark on a more detailed investigation. To this end it is hoped that this book will draw the attention of the new student of the Mollusca to the range of fine works, many of which are listed here, which have been drawn upon in the compilation of the present volume, and all of which have so augmented our understanding of the British molluscan fauna.

Most of the drawings of shells are originals by the author from specimens kindly loaned by the Director of the British Museum (Natural History) and by Mr. Eric Philp from his fine collection of non-marine molluscs in the Maidstone Museum, Kent. Visual access to such collections would prove invaluable to the beginner. Particular thanks are expressed to Roland Smith for his patient drawings of many of the slugs, both terrestrial and marine, and of the cephalopods. John Neville kindly drew the representative chitons, and Maureen Bennett the specimens of *Diodora* and *Patina pellucida v. laevis*. The author and publishers are grateful to several authorities for allowing us to use material; to the Ray Society for permission to redraw certain specimens from Alder and Hancock's classic monograph on the British Nudibranchiate Mollusca, and the supplement by Eliot, to the Trustees of the British Museum (Natural History) for drawings of *Arion ater* from their Zoological Bulletin, to the Editors of the Journal of the Marine species and, slightly amended, species of *Ensis*, to the Editors of Biological Association, U.K., for permission to redraw illustrations of *Spiratella*, *Lutraria angustior* and *L. magna*, certain *Venerupis* the Zoological Society of London for the illustration of radular teeth of *Patella*, to the publishers at the Clarendon Press, Oxford, for allowing us to redraw illustrations of *Testacella* from plates in A. E. Ellis's 'British Snails', to the Editor of L.M.B.C. Memoirs for the drawing of a whelk shell from W. J. Dakin's Memoir XX on *Buccinum*, to the Council of the Malacological Society of London for certain of the illustrations of muscle scars in the Anomiidae, and finally to the Director of the Freshwater Biological Association for permission to redraw in simplified form the illustrations by the late R. D. Cooper of *Hydrobia jenkinsi*, *H. ulvae* and *H. ventrosa* published in T. T. Macan's 'A Key to the British Fresh- and Brackish-water Gastropods' (Scientific Publication No. 13). I am grateful to Professor E. R. Trueman, Dr. V. Fretter, Dr. T. E. Thompson, Dr. M. P. Kerney, and to the Scientific Editor of this Series, Mr. A. R. Kenney, for reading the manuscript and for offering much valuable advice. Finally it is a pleasure to record my appreciation to many colleagues in the Biological Sciences within the North East London Polytechnic for useful discussions and help in many ways, to the photographic section in the College for production of the colour photographs, and to my wife, Margaret, for assistance in preparing the manuscript.

CONTENTS

INTRODUCTION

The molluscs, best known perhaps by the snails, slugs, mussels and clams and by the highly-evolved octopus with its close relatives, the squids, comprise one of the largest and most successful major divisions (phyla) in the animal kingdom. They consist of 80,000 or more species and as such are second only in size to the arthropods. This success is marked by the extent to which the molluscs show great diversity and plasticity of body form and by the widespread and extensive adaptations that they show to a multiplicity of habitats in the sea, in freshwater and on the land.

The typical mollusc, nevertheless, is referable to a common structural plan, and indeed it is probably the adaptability of this basic organisation which has provided the means whereby the evolutionary success of the group has been established. Following its derivation from the Latin *mollis*, the name Mollusca literally means 'soft', emphasizing the spongy texture of the body. Yet in many Mollusca, it is the characteristic shell, usually hard and calcified, varying so widely in form and colour, which typifies the group, so much so that to many people they constitute, with other hard-shelled animals like the crabs and other crustaceans, the rather unfortunately styled 'shell-fish'. For the keen collector the mollusc shell is often the main interest and certainly for identification purposes it is a key structure, particularly where the soft parts of the body have been lost or are withdrawn into the protection of the shell. Nevertheless, a wide variety of well-known molluscs show reduction and in some cases almost complete loss of the shell as, for example, do the slugs, both the terrestrial variety and the often beautifully coloured sea-slugs, and the octopus. To identify molluscs, therefore, one needs to know something of their general anatomy and the way that the form of the body and shell is related.

The basic molluscan form is best visualised in a hypothetical 'archetype' individual as illustrated in fig. 1. This animal is envisaged primitively as a bottom-living marine form showing bilateral symmetry, i.e. one half of the body appearing as a mirror-image of the other

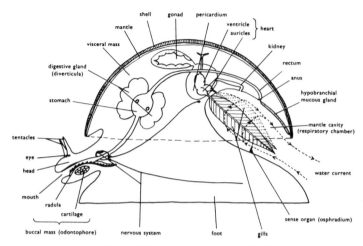

FIG. 1 Diagram of a generalised
archetype mollusc

when viewed from the upper surface. It bears a muscular foot responsible for movement, primitively flat-soled for creeping along the ground,
but like the shell showing much diversity of form throughout the
Mollusca. In front, closely linked with the foot, is the head region
carrying sensory tentacles and also simple eyes. Above the head–foot
region is the visceral mass or hump containing the main organs of the
body, and this is covered by a thin layer of tissue, the mantle or pallium,
which secretes the overlying shell. Enclosed between the mantle/shell
and the rest of the body posteriorly is the important mantle or pallial
cavity, sometimes known as the respiratory chamber, which houses and
protects a pair of respiratory organs, the gills. The incoming water
current bringing oxygen to the gills is tested by a special sense organ
(osphradium), whilst particles and waste materials leaving the respiratory
chamber are compacted in slime produced by a large hypobranchial
mucous gland. In common with the highly adaptable shell and foot, the
mantle cavity is a fundamental source of variation throughout the
Mollusca, ranging from the water-filled respiratory space shown in the
archetype and in many aquatic snails, to the modified air-breathing
lung-like chamber found in the terrestrial snails and slugs, through the
elongated chambers in the bivalves (mussels) containing the enlarged
leaf-like gills used for filter-feeding, to the muscular tube-like cavity in

the squids designed to produce the motive force behind their jet-propulsive movements. Feeding is typically carried out by a rasping, file-like ribbon, the radula, which works by a form of pulley action over a hard piece of cartilaginous tissue, the whole structure constituting the muscular odontophore or buccal mass. The radula, lacking amongst the molluscs only in the bivalves, is protruded through the mouth, the margins of which are protected by horny pads or jaws, and scrapes vegetation from its surroundings. For this purpose it uses numerous rows of teeth on its surface, the nature of which can be used for detailed identification.

The Mollusca, in common with the other major phyla in the animal kingdom, are subdivided into several smaller groups, or classes, each distinguished by certain characteristic features. A complete outline classification of the molluscs described in this volume is given in the Appendix. With the exception of the unique, recently discovered *Neopilina*, found only in the ocean depths and constituting a living relic of a group previously known only as fossils, the unusual worm-like Solenogastres (p. 13), and a rather small specialised class of burrowing forms, the scaphopods, described briefly on page 140, most molluscs likely to be met by the collector will be referable to one of the following classes:

(a) Shell of 8 valves or plates.

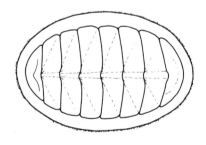

PLACOPHORA (LORICATA) (p. 13)

(b) Shell of 1 valve.

or reduced or absent (slugs)

GASTROPODA (p. 16)

(c) Shell of 2 lateral valves with a dorsal hinge or ligament.

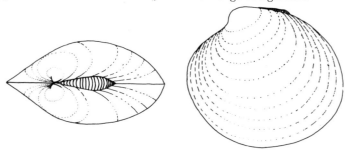

BIVALVIA (p. 141)

(d) Body with arms or tentacles; shell internal, reduced or almost absent.

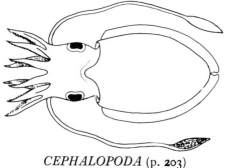

CEPHALOPODA (p. 203)

CLASS: PLACOPHORA [LORICATA]

These rather small and flattened, bilaterally symmetrical animals, commonly known as chitons, or 'coat-of-mail shells', are easily distinguishable from other molluscs by the nature of their shell. This consists of eight, overlapping plates, bordered by a muscular girdle bearing a spiny or bristly cuticle. With the worm-like Solenogastres, a closely-related group of unusual, rather rare molluscs living in deeper water, and in which the shell is represented only by a plate-less cuticle, the chitons constitute a primitive class of Mollusca. They may, indeed, in shell structure, reflect an early stage in molluscan evolution.

Chitons are cleverly adapted to life on the shore. They adhere closely to rocks, usually on the undersurface, or in crevices, and are not always easy to see, being well camouflaged against their background. Once seen, however, chitons are quite unmistakable. There are numerous small gills, probably duplications of the original pair, in grooves down each side of the well-developed foot, which attaches the animal, limpet-like, to the rock surface. If detached from its habitat, the chiton curls itself up like a wood-louse, a manoeuvre made possible by the articulating shell plates, and by so doing protects itself from injury as it is swept about by the waves and water currents on the shore. Chitons feed by rasping vegetation from the rock surface using a long, well-developed radula. The head is small and lacks tentacles and eyes; the animal, however, is quite sensitive and bears unique sense organs (aesthetes) projecting on to the outer surface of the shell plates, sensitive it is believed to touch and in some cases to light.

There are two groups or orders of chitons, the Lepidopleurida, probably more primitive and found mainly off-shore, and the Chitonida, with common intertidal representatives. Accurate identification is based, amongst other features, on the nature of the spines and/or scales borne by the marginal girdle, and the shape and structure of the shell plates. Each plate consists largely of two layers, an outer tegmentum and an inner articulamentum, of which the latter is extended marginally in many chitons into insertion plates embedded in the girdle tissues. Their shape and, for example, whether they are notched or smooth, is often diagnostic and can be seen after carefully freeing the plates from the surrounding tissues and viewing under a microscope or with a hand lens. Comprehensive guides and keys for the identification of all the British species of chiton are given by Gillian Matthews (see Appendix).

The commoner species are as follows:

Lepidopleurus asellus (Gmelin)
Length: 13 mm; *Breadth:* 8 mm.
Diagnostic characters: Girdle narrow and bears small overlapping scales; shell plates lack lateral insertion areas and are smooth marginally without notches; plates raised in mid-line (keeled) and here bear a process (beak), although these features are less marked than in other chitons described below; 8–13 pairs of gills in posterior part only of the groove between mantle and foot (merobranch condition).
Habitat: Mainly off-shore species, representing the primitive lepidopleurids; widely distributed and frequent, attached to rocks, stones and discarded empty shells in deeper water.

Lepidochitona cinereus (L.)
Length: 25 mm; *Breadth:* 16 mm.
Diagnostic characters: Girdle broader and covered with small granules, marginally bearing fine though prominent spines; shell plates bear notched lateral insertion areas; plates prominently beaked and keeled; variably coloured with blotchy mixture of brown, grey or green, sometimes tinged red; 16–19 pairs of gills extending well forward in groove between mantle and foot (holobranch condition).
Habitat: On under surface of rocks and stones, generally distributed on rocky shores; the commonest British chiton. The related *Tonicella rubra* (L.), reddish-brown and 12 mm long, may be found in similar habitats; it has a narrow, granular girdle, and only 10–15 pairs of gills towards posterior end of mantle groove.

Acanthochitona crinitus (Pennant)
Length: 17 mm; *Breadth:* 13 mm.
Diagnostic characters: Girdle broad and bears 18 prominent tufts of bristles; plates with pronounced central keel and marginally notched; very variably-coloured but usually brownish; 10–15 pairs of gills (holobranch).
Habitat: As for *Lepidochitona* but usually towards lower shore; generally distributed but more frequent on south and west coasts; often found lying between other encrusting organisms, e.g. barnacles.

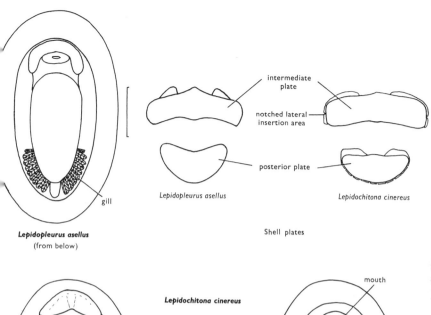

intermediate plate

notched lateral insertion area

posterior plate

Lepidopleurus asellus
(from below)

gill

Lepidopleurus asellus

Lepidochitona cinereus

Shell plates

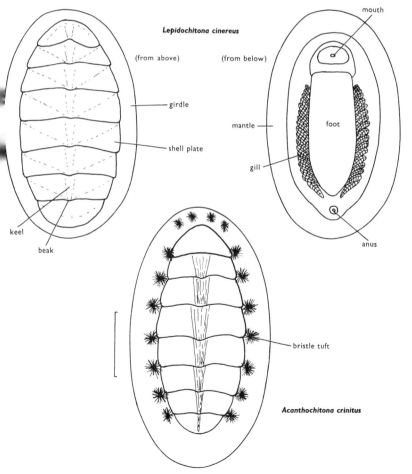

Lepidochitona cinereus

(from above)

girdle

shell plate

keel

beak

(from below)

mouth

mantle

foot

gill

anus

bristle tuft

Acanthochitona crinitus

CLASS: GASTROPODA

The gastropods, characterised by the snails and slugs, are the largest single group (class) of molluscs. In a number of ways they resemble the archetype mollusc, for example, in the possession of a typically broad, flat-soled foot used for crawling, and in the well developed projecting head bearing one or two pairs of sensory tentacles and a pair of eyes (fig. 2). They are distinguished from the early molluscs, however, and indeed from all other molluscan groups, by a basic asymmetry. This is due to a unique feature, known as torsion, in which during development the upper part of the body, including the visceral mass, mantle cavity and shell, is twisted through a half-circle (180°) in an anti-clockwise direction in relation to the head–foot region. This results in the primitively posterior mantle cavity or respiratory chamber, with its contained gills, coming to lie at the anterior end of the animal, just behind and over the head, along with a number of other important changes in the internal body organs. The new position of the mantle cavity and its contained structures in a more advanced snail is shown in fig. 2, in which an efficient left-to-right flow of water through the respiratory chamber has been accomplished by rearrangement of its contents following loss of one of the original pair of gills.

Gastropods with such a forward-facing respiratory chamber are the most primitive members of the group, constituting the Prosobranchia ('front-gilled' forms). They are typically aquatic, found both in the sea, where they are particularly abundant, and in freshwater. Some of the best-known gastropods are marine prosobranchs, including the enormously successful limpets, periwinkles and the whelks. Derived from this primitive group are the Opisthobranchia ('posterior-gilled' ones), a predominantly marine group, aptly named because they show a tendency to undergo unwinding or de-torsion of the visceral hump, with the gills becoming laterally placed or posterior. This process is coupled with secondary loss of the shell, leading ultimately to the sea-hares and the delicate sea-slugs. Finally, there is the well known group, the Pulmonata ('lunged' forms), still showing some effects of torsion, in which the respiratory chamber is modified as a lung-like pulmonary cavity for air-breathing, with a highly vascular wall replacing the gills as a means of obtaining oxygen for respiration. This group is typified by the land snails and the closely allied slugs, and also by aquatic forms,

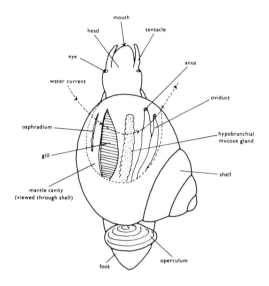

FIG. 2 Typical gastropod viewed
from above

especially the freshwater snails common in ponds and rivers and often
seen in freshwater aquaria. Only a few pulmonates are marine.

In addition to torsion, and probably quite unrelated to it, the typical
gastropod shell, which like that of the archetype is single or univalve,
is usually coiled in a spiral manner as shown in figs. 2, 3 and 4. This
coiling in fact reflects similar coiling of the whole of the visceral mass
and clearly contributes to the compact nature of the body of a typical
snail. Normally the shell is coiled in a right-handed or dextral spiral.
In certain species of snails, however, the shells are coiled in the opposite
direction and are termed left-handed or sinistral. Such a condition may
occur very occasionally due to a rare change or mutation in a normally
right-handed or dextral population of snails. A typical dextrally-coiled
gastropod shell is shown in figs. 2 and 3. With the apex uppermost,
the main opening or aperture of the shell through which the body of the
animal protrudes when extended, is in a dextral shell to the observer's
right; a sinistral shell similarly viewed would have the aperture to the
left.

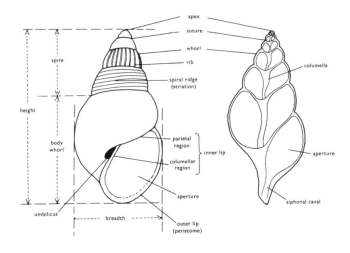

Fig. 3 Diagram of a generalised gastropod shell showing the main features used in measuring and identification

Fig. 4 Half-section of a whelk shell (after Dakin)

As illustrated in figs. 2 and 3, in which the main features used in measuring and identifying the shell are demonstrated, the shell is made up of whorls separated from each other by an indentation or suture, the last and broadest whorl constituting the main or body whorl. The other smaller whorls make up the spire of the shell leading to the apex. It is the nature of this spire in relation to the body whorl which commonly determines the general shape of the shell; for example, it may on the one hand be tall and spired, on the other, relatively flat and disc-shaped. The shell surface may be smooth or variously provided with spirally arranged striations or ridges, or longitudinally raised ribs (fig. 3). The central axis or pillar around which the whorls coil is the columella (best seen in a half-section of the shell, as in fig. 4), forming the basis of attachment in life of the columellar muscle whereby the body is withdrawn into the protection of the shell. When the columella is hollow, the cavity opens at the lower end of the shell as the umbilicus.

The aperture through which the animal emerges is bordered by the outer rim or lip (peristome) and inner (columellar and parietal) lips, which may be smooth, or, as in several snails, lined by teeth which can be of use in identification. In one well-known group, the marine whelks, the aperture is extended into a process, the siphonal canal (fig. 4). Through this in life protrudes a tubular extension of the mantle edge, the siphon, which directs water into the mantle cavity over a well-developed osphradium, and by which the whelks, being carnivorous, can detect the whereabouts of their potential prey (see pp. 54 to 58). In this habit, these snails differ from most gastropods which, rather like the ancestral mollusc, are herbivorous, using the radula to browse on encrusting vegetation and weeds.

When withdrawn into the shell the body is protected by a hardened plug, the operculum, normally borne on the upper surface of the hind end of the foot when the animal is extended, which effectively seals the aperture. This operculum, common in marine snails, but less so in freshwater forms and rare in land snails, may be quite a valuable diagnostic character in the living animal. It should clearly be distinguished from the thin, hardened-mucus pad, known as the epiphragm which is secreted as a protective device across the aperture of many non-operculate terrestrial snails, such as, for example, the common garden snail, *Helix aspersa*, when it is inactive, in adverse conditions or hibernating.

The gastropods, as befits their success, have invaded a multiplicity of habitats in water and on the land. One can for the purposes of identification consider them under three main headings based on habitat; marine, freshwater (including brackish-water forms, i.e. those adapted to living in partly saltwater environments, as in estuaries), and finally terrestrial. In the following pages, each of these groups is dealt with separately, illustrations and descriptions of the main species being preceded in each section by a key to assist in identification. The examples of marine molluscs described here and later in the volume are taken mainly from the sea-shore, which with its unique combination of widely-varying living conditions yet easy accessibility, provides a rich introduction to the fauna of the sea. Some common off-shore species are included, however, both in the keys and illustrative sections, especially where specimens might be encountered washed up on the beach.

Notes on the use of a key

Each key used in this volume is of the dichotomous type consisting of a sequence of numbered statements in pairs which are alternatives, i.e. the specimen being identified is referable to either one or other of the two sets of features described. Starting at 1 and proceeding down the list, the observer decides which of the two alternatives applies to the specimen in question, and then follows the relevant number listed on the right-hand side of the page to the next similarly numbered point on the key. Eventually one reaches the actual name of the specimen or of the group to which it belongs. There will be listed here the Latin scientific name for the animal, using the standard binomial system of nomenclature designed originally by Linnaeus (Linné), giving the name of the genus and species, coupled with the colloquial name by which the mollusc might also be known, for example, *Patella vulgata* L. Common limpet. Popular names are, however, kept to a minimum and the beginner is encouraged to use the specific scientific nomenclature. The name will be accompanied by a page reference number where the particular mollusc will be described in more detail and an illustration given. Here, linked with the scientific name, will be the original author, either written in full, or in the case of the well-known Linnaeus, abbreviated to L.

Where possible, the keys used here adopt natural features, including habitat where the animal is normally found, in addition to obvious morphological characteristics of the shell and/or body, including size and colour. They are, however, artificial in that they do not indicate evolutionary relationships. The limpet-like form, for example, has arisen a number of times independently during the evolution of the gastropods. Some attempt has been made, nevertheless, to deal with the species in a logical sequence. Like all such keys they have to be used flexibly and with caution. Only the more common species or those which illustrate some important facet in the evolutionary history of the Mollusca are described, and attempts to be selective inevitably leave gaps for the more experienced collector. Details of more advanced keys and of works covering a wider range of the British species are given in the

Appendix. The keys adopted here try to avoid detailed anatomical features and rest on a combination of characteristics not all of which may be immediately apparent. Size measurements given can only be used as a general guide since they usually represent the stature of the average adult animal and the observer has to bear in mind the multitude of younger stages which exist, often far smaller than the figures indicate, and yet clearly distinguishable by other morphological characteristics as the species in question. Similarly, colouration of the shell and/or body is often a variable character and should again be viewed with caution. In general, a common-sense approach to the key, rather than a dogmatic acceptance of the features mentioned is advised, and where a specimen clearly keys out to the 'wrong' answer because of a doubt in interpretation of an alternative set of features, the collector is advised to return to the controversial section of the key and try the alternative route. It is, of course, quite possible that the specimen found is of a species not included in this volume because it is relatively rare. With such a large group as the molluscs, of which there are almost 800 British species, it is not possible to describe all the shells in a small volume. The collector should, nevertheless, be able to place it close to its true position by comparison with the species described, and he is encouraged, like all those increasingly aware of the Mollusca as an interesting, adaptive and, in many ways, unusual group, to consult the more comprehensive literature, guides and keys referred to in the Appendix. There is no reason why the collector, especially with interests in a particular group, should not design his own key; this often helps in identifying 'difficult' species which are not easy to separate. Finally, some specimens not commonly encountered in the field and not therefore included in the keys are nevertheless included, and in some cases illustrated, in the general descriptive sections.

Key to Marine Gastropoda

Note: Bracketed sizes in this key indicate shell height.

1. Head bears 1 pair of tentacles; shell typically prominent and
   well·developed (prosobranchs mainly) 2
   Head usually bears 2 pairs of tentacles; shell reduced, commonly internal or absent (mostly opisthobranchs) 38

2. Shell internal, reduced .. .. *Lamellaria perspicua* (p. 52)
   Shell external, well-formed 3

3. Animal lacks operculum 4
   Operculum present* 12

4. Shell coiled (7 whorls), pointed, small (7 mm) and thin-
   walled; pale brown; 3 teeth on inner lip.. *Phytia myosotis*
   (for these and other small marine pulmonates, see p. 74)
   Shell not obviously coiled or with reduced spire, often
   conical or cap-shaped, attached to rocks or weeds, limpet-like 5

5. Shell bearing conspicuous internal ledge or shelf 6
   Shell without internal ledge; typical limpets 7

6. Shell rather oval and arched with horizontal ledge inside posterior half, giving slipper-like appearance; animals often live
   in chains .. .. *Crepidula fornicata* (p. 48)
   Shell round, flattened, thin-walled, with small pointed apex;
   bearing oblique, twisted shelf inside rear part; animals single
   Calyptraea chinensis (p. 48)

7. Limpets with opening(s) or slit in shell 8
   Limpets with complete shell 9

8. Shell with series of openings .. *Haliotis tuberculata* (p. 30)
   Shell with marginal slit .. .. .. *Emarginula* spp. (p. 30)
   Shell with single apical opening .. .. *Diodora apertura* (p. 30)

9. Shell with ribbed surface and ridged margin 10
   Shell surface and margin usually smooth 11

*This distinction may be difficult to make, especially if the shell only is avail-
able; for practical purposes it can be assumed that if the shell is not limpet-like
then, with the exception of the pulmonates (4 above) and certain snails not
dealt with here, most marine snails typically bear an operculum.

10. Shell usually rather tall, conical, strongly-ribbed, inner surface white to yellow; head scar silvery-nacreous or opaque white; foot light greyish-green; marginal tentacles lack pigment; abundant ..   ..   *Patella vulgata* Common limpet (p. 34)
Shell typically less conical, finer ribs, inner surface dark, margin strongly marked with chocolate-brown rays; head scar cream, or darker, tinged orange; foot dark grey-green; marginal tentacles chalky white   ..   ..
Patella intermedia [*P. depressa*] (p. 34)
Shell also somewhat flattened, inner surface white, porcellanous, usually lacking marginal rays; head scar yellow to orange; foot pale creamy-orange; marginal tentacles cream
Patella aspera [*P. athletica*] (p. 34)

11. Shell bearing bright blue lines; ring of secondary gills around mantle edge   ..   ..   *Patina pellucida* (p. 32)
Shell a flat cone with irregular tortoise-shell pattern of reddish-brown markings; single anterior gill; northern coasts   ..
Acmaea tessulata (p. 32)
Similar, but shell whitish with pink rays, generally distributed   ..   ..   *Acmaea virginea* (p. 32)

12. Body whorl covers other whorls; aperture forms longitudinal slit   ..   ..   *Trivia* spp. (p. 52)
Shell more typically snail-like with distinct whorls   13

13. Shell with siphonal canal (see fig. 4), through which siphon from mantle projects; thick shells, sculptured with pointed spires (whelks)   14
Siphonal canal absent   18

14. Siphonal canal closed in adult; shell rugged, with strong, wavy ribs   ..   ..   *Ocenebra erinacea* (p. 54)
Siphonal canal open; ribs, where present, less rugged and more regular   15

15. Shell often large (100 mm, although smaller on shore), with whorls well sculptured and a clearly defined suture; large oval aperture and wide siphonal canal ..   ..
Buccinum undatum Common whelk (p. 56)

Shell smaller, suture less well defined; aperture smaller with narrower siphonal canal 16

16. Shell thick, forming a short cone; mature shell lacks longi-tudinal ribs, but spirally-ridged; often pale-coloured but may be banded; very common   *Nucella lapillus* Dog whelk (p. 54)
Shell slimmer with taller spire; longitudinal ribs present   .. 17

17. Shell (28 mm) with network of intersecting ridges and ribs on surface; often on sandy areas   ..   *Nassarius reticulatus* (p. 58)
Shell smaller (12 mm), whorls more rounded with pronounced longitudinal ribs; brown mark on base; usually on rocky surfaces   ..   ..   *Nassarius incrassatus* (p. 58)

18. Sand-burrower with globular polished shell; small spire; prominent umbilicus; large foot partly reflected over shell .. 19
Not a sand-burrower on shore; shell otherwise shaped or coloured 20

19. Shell (14 mm) bears 5 rows of reddish-brown streaks or spots on body whorl; pad protrudes into upper part of umbilicus
Natica alderi (p. 50)
Shell twice as high; umbilicus large and unobtruded; one row of reddish-brown streaks on upper side of each whorl   ..
Natica catena (p. 50)

20. Broad-based shells shaped like tops; foot bears lateral ten-tacular processes; umbilicus often prominent (top shells) 21
(see also *Tricolia* below, p. 25)
Shells not typically top-shaped; foot without lateral processes 26

21. Shell tiny (4 mm), pale orange-brown, northern coasts only
Margarites helicinus (p. 36)
Shell larger   22

22. Shell flat sided and pointed, pyramid-like or conical; no umbilicus   23
Shell blunter, umbilicus may be well marked 24

23. Shell large (25 mm), pyramid shaped, with broad flat base;
    10–12 whorls, red streaks on lighter background   ..   ..
                                Calliostoma zizyphinum (p. 38)
    Shell smaller, with narrower base, 6–8 whorls. .   ..   ..
                                      Cantharidus spp. (p. 38)

24. Shell with umbilicus almost covered; large (18 mm), apex
    eroded, tooth on inner (columellar) side of aperture ..   ..
                                  Monodonta lineata (p. 38)
    Shell with umbilicus clearly visible   25

25. Shell large (19 mm), solid with keel on ridge at base; reddish
    streaks on yellow background; very wide umbilicus ..   ..
                                      Gibbula magus (p. 36)
    Shell smaller (12 mm), bluntly conical; background colour light
    grey marked with darker narrow stripes; small, narrow
    umbilicus; on lower part of shore   ..   *Gibbula cineraria* (p. 36)
    Shell generally flatter, broader (18 mm), than tall (13 mm),
    background colour greenish with prominent broad purplish
    stripes; umbilicus larger than *G. cineraria*; middle shore   ..
                                Gibbula umbilicalis (p. 36)

26. Rounded or conical shells   27
    Shells elongate with tall spires   31

27. Shell with white, limy operculum; small (9 mm tall), conical;
    yellow with reddish markings; foot bears sensory tentacles
    (see also 20 above)   ..   ..   ..   *Tricolia pullus* (p. 38)
    Operculum horny, ear-shaped   28

28. Shell with slit-like umbilicus   ..   ..   *Lacuna* spp. (p. 42)
    Shell without umbilicus (winkles or periwinkles)   29

29. Shell not pointed, flat-topped, colour very variable; found
    on fucoid seaweeds; mid- to lower-shore; common ..   ..
                                Littorina littoralis (p. 42)
    Shell pointed   30

30. Shell small (6 mm), fragile; outer lip flexible; dark with
characteristic bloom; in splash zone   *Littorina neritoides* (p. 40)
Shell larger (12 mm), more robust
and rough with wrinkles on surface;
curve of aperture meets body whorl at
right angle; upper shore, common   ..
Littorina saxatilis (p. 40)
Largest forms (25 mm), blackish with
concentric dark lines; curve of aperture
meets body whorl obliquely; mid-to
lower-shore; abundant ..   ..   ..
Littorina littorea Common or edible periwinkle (p. 40)

31. Shell very small, typically 4–5 mm or less in height 32
    Shell taller   33

32. Shell often strongly ribbed; outer lip of aperture typically
strengthened by a white rib   ..   ..   *Rissoa* spp. (p. 44)
   (One common species, *R. parva*, 4–5 mm tall, is distinguishable by a characteristic brown, comma-shaped mark
near the outer lip of the aperture.)
Shell smooth or with spiral striations; outer lip commonly
without rib   ..   ..   *Cingula* spp. (p. 44)
   (A typical species, *C. cingillus*, is 4 mm tall and with a
brown-banded shell.)

33. Shell surface smooth   34
    Shell sculptured 35

34. Shell small (6 mm), brownish, typically with six flattened
whorls; abundant on mud surface in estuaries and salt
marshes ..   ..   *Hydrobia ulvae*
   (For this and related brackish-water species, see p. 82.)
Shell elongate, variable height with very smooth, polished
surface; often white; off-shore species associated with echinoderms   ..   ..   *Balcis* spp. (p. 46)
   (One quite common species, *B. alba*, has a solid ivory-
white, 17 mm tall shell.)

35. Shell small, not usually more than 13 mm tall, needle-shaped   36
    Shell larger and heavier 37

36. Shell (10 mm) needle-shaped, 15–16 whorls with criss-cross sculpture produced by intersection of ribs and spiral striations
Bittium reticulatum (p. 46)
Shell (8 mm) elongate and slender but solid, whitish; up to 12 whorls with 20–25 obliquely-curved ribs; associated with worms, e.g. *Amphitrite* at low water in silt or sand .. ..
Turbonilla elegantissima (p. 60)

37. Shell turret-shaped with outer lip of aperture expanded to form processes giving shape like pelican's foot; washed up on shore .. .. *Aporrhais pes-pelecani* (p. 50)
Shell tall (50 mm) tapering, 16–20 whorls, many spirally-ridged; commonly washed up as empty shells on shore ..
Turritella communis (p. 46)
Shell tall (37 mm), 15–16 whorls, conspicuously ribbed; usually only seen as empty shells .. *Clathrus clathrus* (p. 46)

38. Operculum present; shell still well-developed, barrel-shaped, pink or brown with white bands; animal itself not commonly seen on shore .. .. .. *Acteon tornatilis* (p. 58)
No operculum 39

39. Shell external, reduced, thin and white, partly covered in life by body tissues; foot with upwardly directed mottled lobes (parapodia) used for swimming .. .. *Akera bullata* (p. 60)
Shell reduced and internally enclosed in mantle, or absent .. 40

40. Shell reduced, more or less hidden within body; with or without parapodia 41
Shell absent; commonly with gills or other processes on back, but no parapodia (nudibranchs or sea-slugs) 44

41. Parapodia present 42
Parapodia absent; feathery gill prominent on right-hand side 43

42. Brownish or olive-green body, variously spotted; posterior tentacles ear-shaped; produces purplish slime .. ..
Aplysia punctata Sea hare (p. 62)
Body (and internal shell) white; in four lobes, one anterior, two lateral (parapodia) and one posterior (mantle) .. ..
Philine quadripartita (p. 62)

43. Back reddish-brown and covered with tubercles   ..   ..
        Pleurobranchus membranaceus (p. 64)
    Body smooth and yellow   ..   .. *Berthella plumula* (p. 64)

44. Body small (6 mm long), smooth, without dorsal processes or
    gills,; elongated lateral flaps; green with lighter spots; associ-
    ated with green seaweeds   ..   .. *Elysia viridis* (p. 64)
    Body with gills and/or other processes   45

45. Body with ring of gills around anus; lacks distinct dorsal
    processes (cerata) on back although body may bear lateral
    processes   46
    Body with elongate or branched dorsal processes (cerata);
    usually lacking gills or other processes   52

46. Ring of gills around anus can be withdrawn into cavity in
    mantle (retractile)   47
    Gills not retractile   48

47. Animal large (70 mm long), with 9 prominent, plumed gills;
    surface of back rough (tuberculate); mainly yellow, but
    variously mottled with other colours   ..   ..
        Archidoris pseudoargus Sea lemon (p. 66)
    Somewhat smaller, and less common; also yellowish, but
    smoother and with 11–15 white gills   .. *Jorunna tomentosa* (p. 66)
    Smooth, white with 5 small gills; 25 mm long; north-
    eastern coasts only   ..   ..   .. *Cadlina laevis* (p. 66)

48. Certain prominent coloured processes on body in addition to
    the non-retractile gills   49
    Gills only present   50

49. Body whitish (15 mm long) with rows of yellow tubercles;
    2 prominent yellow-tipped processes directed backwards on
    each side of 7–9 gills, also similar processes bordering head
        Polycera quadrilineata (p. 70)
    Body similar size and ground colour but more flattened and
    with only 3 gills; no long processes bordering gills (contrast
    Polycera) but processes around margin of body tipped deep
    yellow, also deep yellow tubercles on back   ..   ..   ..
        Limacia clavigera (p. 70)

50. Mantle reduced, indented posteriorly; keel down centre of
    body   ..   ..   *Goniodoris nodosa* (p. 68)
    Mantle forms complete cloak on upper surface   51

51. Short, plump tubercles on mantle; 20 gills form circle in-
    complete behind anus   ..   ..   .. *Onchidoris fusca* (p. 68)
    Tall, soft-looking tubercles on mantle, 9 gills ..   ..   ..
                                        Acanthodoris pilosa (p. 70)

52. Cerata very branched   ..   .. *Dendronotus frondosus* (p. 70)
    Cerata unbranched   53

53. Body large (up to 75 mm long), covered with dense, felt-like
    mass of cerata; common   ..   *Aeolidia papillosa* (p. 72)
    Smaller (25 mm long), cerata reddish, in 4–6 clusters   ..
                                        Facelina auriculata (p. 72)
    Smaller still (12 mm long), with 5–7 pairs of large cerata;
    body pale with crimson markings   .. *Doto coronata* (p. 74)

Haliotis tuberculata L.

Length: 85 mm; *Breadth:* 60 mm; *Height:* 18 mm.

Diagnostic characters: Shell very flattened with a reduced spire and pierced by a series of holes; those most recently-formed openings, usually five or six in number, are near the anterior end and perforate the shell completely; the remainder, which are the oldest ones, are closed and non-functional.

Habitat: On rocks near low-water mark and below; not strictly a British species but quite frequent in the Channel Islands.

General features: Rather a 'fringe' species more typical of warmer Mediterranean waters, but worth including because, with the slit and keyhole limpets described below, it constitutes one of the most primitive of living gastropods. These retain a pair of gills and typically have shells which are perforated with notches or holes. The openings have a sanitary function and ensure that the waste products contained in the water leaving the mantle cavity are directed upwards well away from the head region. The shell of *Haliotis* (the ormer), which shines beautifully when cleaned and polished, has decorative uses, whilst the flesh of the animal is an edible delicacy.

Diodora apertura (Montagu)

Length: 25 mm; *Breadth:* 15 mm; *Height:* 10 mm.

Diagnostic characters: Conical shell with keyhole opening in apex (hence the popular name 'keyhole limpet'; in life, the opening bears a spout-like process of the mantle); surface ribbed, no spiral coiling.

Habitat: On rocky surfaces at low-water mark and below; more common in south and west.

General features: Like all limpets with perforated shells this species is restricted to the lowest part of the shore where there is less danger of desiccation; these forms cannot compete with the common limpet, *Patella vulgata* (see p. 34) with its complete, water-tight shell, on more exposed regions of the intertidal zone.

Emarginula reticulata Sowerby

Length: 10 mm; *Breadth:* 7 mm; *Height:* 7 mm.

Diagnostic characters: White ribbed shell with notch or slit on the anterior margin ('slit limpet'); apex slightly curved backwards (the related *E. conica* Lamarck, an off-shore species, is distinguished by a smaller shell with a much more curved, forwardly directed, apex).

Habitat: Widely distributed; on rocks and stones at low water and below.

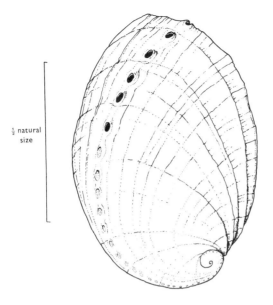

½ natural size

Haliotis tuberculata

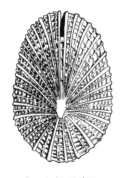

Emarginula reticulata

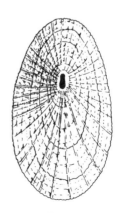

Diodora apertura

Acmaea tessulata (Müller)

Length: 12 mm; *Breadth:* 9 mm; *Height:* 4 mm.

Diagnostic characters: Delicate smooth shell, constituting a rather flattened cone, with the apex anterior to the mid-line; marked by characteristic, reddish-brown tortoise-shell pattern on surface; single prominent gill in cavity behind the head.

Habitat: Under stones near low-water or in rock pools; not on exposed rocks; found only on northern coasts.

General features: Although with an imperforate shell, *Acmaea*, the so-called tortoise-shell limpet, still shows primitive features, for example, the plumed gill, and it inhabits sheltered areas.

Acmaea virginea (Müller)

Length: 12 mm; *Breadth:* 10 mm; *Height:* 5 mm.

Diagnostic characters: Similar in shape and structure to *A. tessulata*, but with a paler, slightly stronger shell, bearing delicate pinkish rays.

Habitat: Under stones at low water in the *Laminaria* zone and also off-shore; widely distributed.

Patina pellucida (L.)

Length: v. pellucida 10 mm; *Breadth:* 6 mm; *Height:* 2.5 mm.
 v. laevis   19 mm;   16 mm;   6 mm.

Diagnostic characters: Smooth, generally conical shell, marked by vivid blue rays (2–8, typically 3–5 in younger shells) running from the apex to the posterior margin; no true gills but a ring of secondary gills is developed from around the pallial (mantle) skirt, except anterior to the head.

Habitat: Common at low water on *Laminaria:* widely distributed.

General features: This beautifully-coloured limpet with its bright blue, sometimes iridescent greenish, markings on a pale brown background, exists in two varieties. One, *pellucida*, with a smooth, translucent, low and rather oval shell, lives on the fronds of *Laminaria*; the other, *laevis*, with a rougher, taller and more circular shell, on which the blue rays are less clearly marked, is found in sheltered cavities in the holdfast. In the youngest stages, the shell is always of the *pellucida* type. Those individuals, however, which find their way into confined spaces in the holdfast subsequently develop shell of the *laevis* variety, the change in appearance often being clearly marked.

Acmaea tessulata

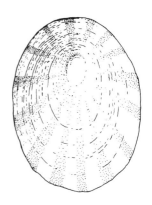

Acmaea virginea

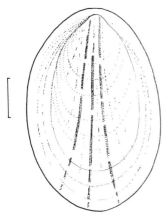

Patina pellucida v. pellucida

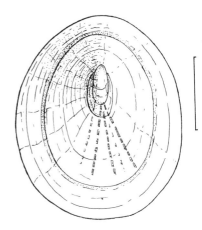

Patina pellucida v. laevis

Patella vulgata L.   Common limpet

Length: 55 mm; *Breadth:* 45 mm; *Height:* 20 mm.

Diagnostic characters: Shell strong, cone-shaped, usually rather tall, but varies; strong ribs externally with ridged margin; colour yellowish-green but very variable; internal surface white or yellowed; head scar (mark left towards crown of shell after removing body) silvery-nacreous or opaque white; foot light greyish-green; marginal tentacles of mantle transparent, lacking white pigment; ring of secondary gills all around the mantle (pallial) skirt.

Habitat: Abundant on all rocky shores, both on exposed surfaces and in pools, feeding on encrusted algae.

General features: Patella is one of the most fully adapted of all molluscs to life on exposed rocky shores, where it lives intimately attached by the large foot to its 'home' on the rock surface. Shell form varies appreciably and to distinguish the common limpet accurately from the two other British species, one needs to study the inner shell surface and head scar, and the animal itself, including if possible the radula and its teeth.

Patella intermedia Jeffreys [*P. depressa* Pennant]

Length: 27 mm; *Breadth:* 23 mm; *Height:* 10 mm.

Diagnostic characters: Shell generally flatter and more oval than *P. vulgata* with finer ribs; smaller than both other species; inner surface dark with chocolate-brown rays at margin; head scar cream, sometimes darker or orange-tinged; dark green-grey foot and body; marginal tentacles of mantle chalk-white and opaque.

Habitat: S.W. coasts only, in exposed areas, mainly on middle shore where it overlaps with *P. vulgata*; rarely extends into the upper shore, however, where the common limpet dominates.

Patella aspera Lamarck [*P. athletica* Bean]

Length: 45 mm; *Breadth:* 38 mm; *Height:* 17 mm.

Diagnostic characters: Shell also flatter than *P. vulgata* with apex nearer the anterior end; fine ribs; inner surface white and porcellanous, with head scar yellow to orange; marginal rays usually lacking; foot pale creamy-orange; marginal tentacles of mantle cream-coloured.

Habitat: More widely distributed than *P. intermedia*, extending beyond S.W. coasts, also on exposed areas but generally lower on the shore than species described above, favouring wetter places, including shallow pools; often found associated with calcareous red algae, e.g. *Corallina* and *Lithothamnion*, in pools encrusted with the latter sometimes higher on the shore.

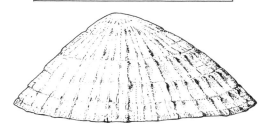

Patella vulgata

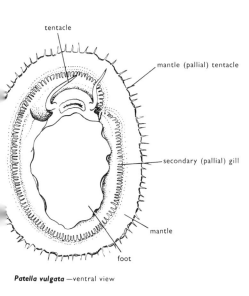

Patella vulgata—ventral view

tentacle

mantle (pallial) tentacle

secondary (pallial) gill

mantle

foot

P. vulgata

P. intermedia

P. aspera

Radular teeth
(pluricuspid)—after Evans

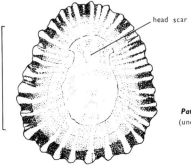

head scar

Patella intermedia
(underside of shell)

Margarites helicinus (Fabricius)

Height: 4 mm; *Breadth:* 5 mm.

Diagnostic characters: Shell small, thin, smooth-surfaced, with a rather low spire; orange-brown; broad umbilicus; foot bears lateral epipodial tentacles (6 pairs).

Habitat: Hidden amongst weed under rocks, near low water; northern coasts only; the larger (8 mm) *M. groenlandicus* (Gmelin) with a more sculptured surface, occurs more frequently in deeper water, mainly off north-west Scotland.

General features: This is one of the least specialised of the Trochidae family of snails, popularly known as top shells, including *Gibbula* to *Cantharidus* below. These gastropods show primitive features, e.g. in shell form, the structure of the gills, and the presence of delicate sensory (epipodial) tentacles borne by the foot.

Gibbula cineraria (L.)

Height: 12 mm; *Breadth:* 14 mm.

Diagnostic characters: Shell variable in size but usually as high as it is broad, shaped like a blunt spinning-top; 6–7 whorls; pale grey with very narrow, dark purple-brown or dark grey streaks or stripes; small, narrow umbilicus.

Habitat: Widely distributed; found in clean, sheltered habitats, in pools or amongst seaweeds, on all rocky shores, mainly lower half of shore; very common, especially on east coast.

Gibbula umbilicalis (da Costa)

Height: 13 mm; *Breadth:* 18 mm.

Diagnostic characters: Shell broader than tall, appearing therefore flatter than in *G. cineraria;* background more greenish with fewer, wider, reddish or purplish stripes; larger umbilicus (see opposite).

Habitat: Generally similar to *G. cineraria* but extends further up the shore tolerating greater exposure, ranging through the middle and upper part of the lower shore; mainly on S and W coasts, common.

Gibbula magus (L.)

Height: 19 mm; *Breadth:* 26 mm.

Diagnostic characters: Thick, large, rather flattened shell with an angular (keeled) base; whorls appear high-shouldered with swollen ribs on upper side; yellowish-white with pink markings; very broad umbilicus.

Habitat: On rocks at extreme low water, but mainly off-shore on muddy sand or gravel; south and west coasts, also Ireland; the smaller (10 mm), turreted *G. tumida* (Montagu), occurs only in deeper water.

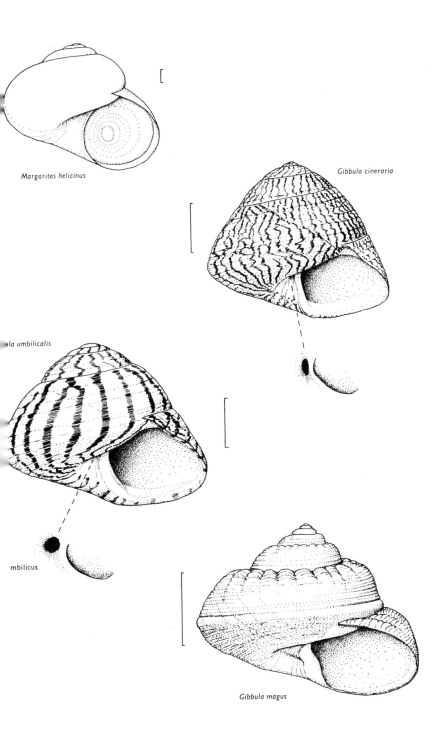

Margarites helicinus

Gibbula cineraria

la umbilicalis

mbilicus

Gibbula magus

Monodonta lineata (da Costa)

Height: 18 mm; *Breadth:* 18 mm.

Diagnostic characters: Shell thick, solid, rounded, 6 whorls; apex often worn away exposing underlying shell, yellow or silvery in colour; grey to greenish background colour with zig-zag dark purple streaks; aperture with prominent process (tooth) on inner side; umbilicus almost hidden in adult.

Habitat: South-western rocky shores where may be locally common, also most of Ireland; middle shore on more exposed habitats than other top shells (tends to be adversely affected by hard winters).

Calliostoma zizyphinum (L.)

Height: 25 mm; *Breadth:* 25 mm.

Diagnostic characters: Shell large and brightly coloured forming an almost regular pyramid shape with platform-like base; 8–10 whorls with spirally ridged surface; usually pale yellow or pink with reddish-brown streaks; body tissues also brightly pigmented; no umbilicus.

Habitat: Widely distributed on rocky shores, low-water mark and below; more frequent on southern and western coasts.

Cantharidus striatus (L.)

Height: 10 mm; *Breadth:* 7.5 mm.

Diagnostic characters: Shell flat-sided forming a small, pointed cone; ridged surface; pale with brownish or other coloured markings.

Habitat: Associated with *Zostera* (eel-grass), extreme low water and off-shore; south-west England and southern Ireland (other species, for example, the larger, 15 mm tall, *C. clelandi* (Wood), occur in deeper water off-shore).

Tricolia pullus (L.)

Height: 9 mm; *Breadth:* 6 mm.

Diagnostic characters: Shell small, solid and conical; 5–6 whorls, the body whorl being taller than rest of shell; glossy surface, usually yellowish with red or purple, often zig-zag, markings; prominent white calcareous operculum; sensory tentacular processes on sides of foot.

Habitat: Low-water mark in rock pools on weed, particularly on the matching red alga *Chondrus* from which its red shell pigments may derive; mainly southern and western coasts.

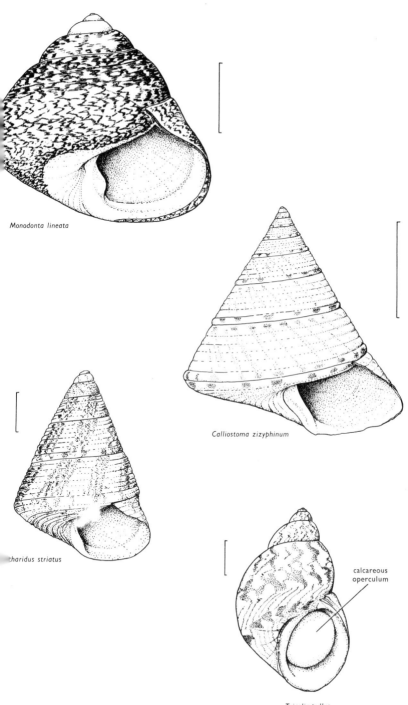

Monodonta lineata

Calliostoma zizyphinum

...haridus striatus

calcareous
operculum

Tricolia pullus

Littorina littorea (L.)   Common or edible winkle or periwinkle
Height: 26 mm; *Breadth:* 20 mm.

Diagnostic characters: Shell dark brown to almost black, sometimes banded concentrically; 6–7 rather flattened whorls, spire somewhat long and pointed; lip of aperture meets body whorl at tangent; tentacles cross-striped with black; horny, ear-shaped operculum (feature of all *Littorina* and *Lacuna* species—see fig. of *L. neritoides* opposite).

Habitat: Widely distributed on all rocky shores, on rocks or near scattered weeds, and even on silted or sandy regions, tending to avoid densely-weeded areas; middle shore to low water, abundant.

General features: The common or edible periwinkle is one of the most successful and prolific of intertidal snails and is widely collected for food. This and the other three species of *Littorina*, the latter non-edible and much smaller, but equally hardy (see below), colonise different, although widely overlapping, regions of almost all rocky shores, a feature known as zonation.

Littorina saxatilis (Olivi)

Height: 12 mm; *Breadth:* 10 mm.

Diagnostic characters: Shell with 6–9 whorls, suture deep; surface rough with spiral ridges; variably-coloured, sometimes banded (shell form varies; for details of named subspecies and varieties of *L. saxatilis* see work of James referred to in Appendix); outer lip of aperture meets body whorl at right angle; longitudinal stripes on tentacles; bears young alive (viviparous).

Habitat: Widely distributed on all rocky shores; upper half of shore in cracks and crevices (resistant to exposure), very common.

Littorina neritoides (L.)

Height: 7 mm; *Breadth:* 6 mm.

Diagnostic characters: Shell pointed, narrow, 5–6 whorls, rather fragile; outer lip of aperture flexible; smooth, dark surface.

Habitat: In rock crevices on uppermost part of the shore, i.e. in the splash zone; widely distributed, common.

General features: This, the smallest periwinkle, is the *Littorina* species most resistant to exposure and it can survive desiccation in the splash zone at and above high-water mark for long periods. Spawning is geared to certain particularly high spring tides, the animals migrating some way down the shore to shed their egg capsules.

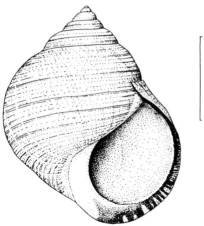

Littorina littorea

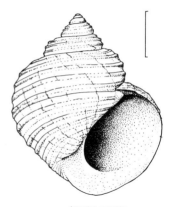

Littorina saxatilis

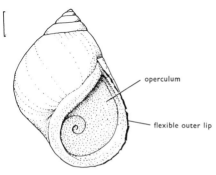

operculum

flexible outer lip

Littorina neritoides

Littorina littoralis (L.)

Height: 12 mm; *Breadth:* 13 mm.

Diagnostic characters: Shell rounded, spire much blunter; 5 whorls, the last (body) whorl making up most of the shell; great variability of colour from yellow to dark brown or banded.

Habitat: Widely distributed on most rocky shores, especially if sheltered; found mainly in wet places, on fucoid seaweeds and in pools on the middle shore and upper part of lower shore; very common.

General features: This species is clearly distinguished by form (characteristic flat-topped shell) and by habitat (favours seaweeds, mainly *Fucus vesiculosus* and *Ascophyllum*) from other periwinkles. The weeds are required for food and for providing a continually moist atmosphere when exposed by the tide. The whole life cycle, commencing with the gelatinous egg-capsules laid on the fronds, is conducted in and around these seaweeds. The spawn masses appear as characteristic flattened, circular, oval or kidney-shaped patches on the surface of the weed. The various colour patterns which characterise individuals of the species may be genetically determined and distinct. Up to 12 varieties have been described, some evenly-coloured (e.g. green, yellow or reddish-orange) and others banded or finely patterned.

Lacuna vincta (Montagu)

Height: 12 mm; *Breadth:* 7 mm.

Diagnostic characters: Shell of 6 whorls, small and conical; shiny surface, yellowish with well-marked reddish-brown bands; umbilicus elongated and slit-like (this feature separates *Lacuna*, the so-called 'chink shell', from species of *Littorina*); a pair of characteristic (metapodial) tentacles protrude from rear of foot.

Habitat: Widely distributed on rocky shores on red, brown or green seaweeds; lower shore and off-shore.

General features: This small, beautifully coloured snail is quite closely-related to the periwinkles but generally less hardy and restricted to the lower shore. The much smaller (5 mm), more swollen, *L. parva* (da Costa) is also found at extreme low water, but is less widely distributed, whilst the even more globular, unbanded (10 mm) *L. pallidula* (da Costa) and much larger (18 mm), turreted, *L. crassior* (Montagu) frequent deeper waters.

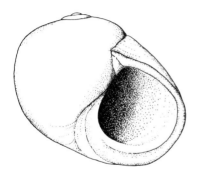

Littorina littoralis

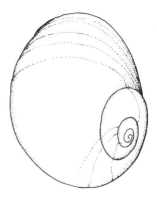

Littorina littoralis (from upper surface)

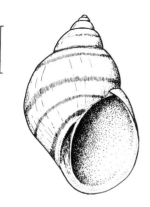

Lacuna vincta

Rissoa parva (da Costa)

Height: 4 mm; *Breadth:* 2 mm.

Diagnostic characters: Shell very small, pointed, 6–7 whorls, some populations with strong longitudinal ribs, but this is a variable feature; outer lip with supporting white rib; colour pale, often with purple-brown apex and with characteristic comma-shaped brown streak on base of body whorl.

Habitat: Mid to lower shore and below, mainly on weeds and stones; on all coasts.

General features: This snail and *Cingula* (see below) may be regarded as representative of the large family of minute marine snails, the Rissoidae, often missed because of their very small size and preference for sheltered habitats amongst weeds or in silty areas. *R. parva* can be extremely common on some rocky shores. It is an active herbivorous snail feeding on diatoms or algal fragments. Other species quite frequently found include the taller (7 mm) *R. membranacea* (J. Adams), typically associated with *Zostera* (eel-grass). Many other species, e.g. those of *Alvania*, are more typically found off-shore. Other related forms of this successful family are the brackish-water hydrobiid snails described later on p. 82.

Cingula cingillus (Montagu)

Height: 4 mm; *Breadth:* 2 mm.

Diagnostic characters: Shell tiny, conical, solid; pale, with characteristic deep brownish bands; six flattish whorls.

Habitat: In rocky crevices and pools and under stones, also in empty barnacle shells, mainly in silted areas; mid-shore or higher, but also found in deeper water; widely distributed.

General features: This is one of the commonest of several species of *Cingula* found both on the shore and in deeper water. The paler, relatively unbanded, *C. semicostata* (Montagu), lives in similar habitats inter-tidally. Along with these rissoids, the keen collector might search for even tinier species from certain closely-related families; these include *Cingulopsis* (1.5 mm tall), and the miniscule, flattened *Skeneopsis planorbis* (Fabricius), species of *Rissoella*, and the nicely named *Omalogyra atomus* (Philippi), minute and disc-like, all 1.5 mm or less in diameter, but frequenting rock pools on many shores.

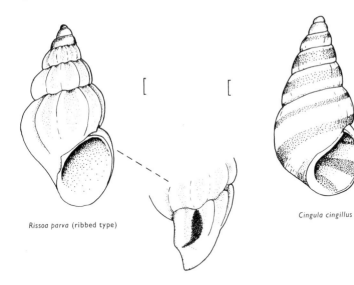

Rissoa parva (ribbed type)

Cingula cingillus

Omalogyrus atomus

Skeneopsis planorbis

Bittium reticulatum (da Costa)

Height: 10 mm; *Breadth:* 3 mm.

Diagnostic characters: Shell tall and pointed, comprising 15–16 whorls; criss-cross tubercled surface produced by prominent ribs crossing spiral ridges; brownish; no umbilicus.

Habitat: Under rocks on rubbish; lower shore and below; forms an egg-mass shaped like a miniature catherine-wheel fastened flat to the surface of the weed where it lives; widely distributed.

General features: These small needle-like snails live in habitats similar to the rissoids described above, feeding on encrusting algae and detritus. Similarly shaped, but smaller still and more frequently found off-shore, are species of *Cerithiopsis*, and the unusual *Triphora perversa* (L.), the only prosobranch snail with a true sinistral (left-handed) shell.

Clathrus clathrus (L.)

Height: 37 mm; *Breadth:* 13 mm.

Diagnostic characters: Shell tall, 15–16 whorls, handsomely sculptured with deep suture and conspicuous longitudinal ribs (9 on body whorl); pale cream or fawn.

Habitat: Muddy sand, usually off-shore, but occasionally at low water mark feeding may-be on sea-anemones; more often found in south-west.

Turritella communis Risso

Height: 54 mm; *Breadth:* 15 mm.

Diagnostic characters: Shell long, with 16–19 whorls, spirally ridged; pale or yellow-brown.

Habitat: Burrows in muddy ground off-shore where it is often gregarious and locally frequent; empty shells found on beach; widely distributed.

Balcis alba (da Costa)

Length: 17 mm; *Breadth:* 5 mm.

Diagnostic characters: Shell solid, ivory-coloured with very smooth flat-sided surface; up to 18 whorls; animal with yellow markings.

Habitat: Off-shore species, widely distributed; associated with echinoderms, typically the sea-urchin *Spatangus*.

General features: This species is a typical representative of a family of marine snails, the eulimids, ectoparasitic on echinoderms. They all have characteristically elongated and very shiny shells. The much smaller (3 mm) *B. devians* (Monterosato) with a more curved spire, lives associated with the sea-star, *Antedon*.

Bittium reticulatum

Clathrus clathrus

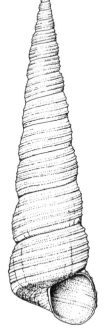

Turritella communis

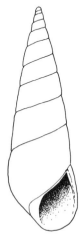

Balcis alba

Crepidula fornicata (L.)   Slipper limpet

Height: 16 mm; *Length:* 40 mm; *Breadth:* 28 mm.

Diagnostic characters: Shell oval, off-white or brownish, variable height
   but with a characteristic curled apex; prominent internal horizontal
   ledge which extends half way across shell giving slipper-like appearance from underside; forms chains of animals up to 12 in number.

Habitat: In quiet estuarine localities, especially on oyster beds, on
   eastern and southern coasts, particularly in S.E. England.

General features: This prolific limpet-like form, more closely related to
   the periwinkles than to the true limpets, is in fact an introduced
   species and has become a serious pest on oyster beds. Imported from
   the United States in the late nineteenth century along with American
   oysters it competes with the native oyster for food and settlement sites.
   Like the oyster, the slipper limpet is an accomplished suspension or
   ciliary feeder. *Crepidula* can actually settle on top of the oysters,
   almost smothering them and forming a thick carpet. This feature is
   enhanced by the unusual habit of the slipper limpets living in chains,
   one individual on top of the other; the lower, older specimens are
   female and are fertilised by the upper, younger male individuals, the
   animal changing sex, therefore, as it grows.

Calyptraea chinensis (L.)

Height: 6 mm; *Length:* 14 mm; *Breadth:* 14 mm.

Diagnostic characters: Shell thin, rounded, forming a low, flattened cone
   with a central apex; whitish; internally there is an oblique, twisted
   shelf projecting across the posterior region of the shell.

Habitat: Low-water mark and off-shore, on the underside of shells or
   stones; south-western coasts, also Channel Islands.

General features: This is a native species related to the slipper limpet
   with similar feeding habits. As in *Crepidula*, *Calyptraea* individuals
   change from male to female as they grow, but unlike the slipper
   limpet they do not live in chains; functional males and females are
   only associated during the breeding season. Another limpet-like form,
   but lacking an internal shelf, is *Capulus ungaricus* (L.), with a characteristically shaped bonnet-like shell; it is, however, confined to
   deeper waters, usually attached to scallop shells.

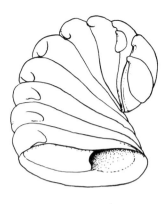

Crepidula—chain of individuals

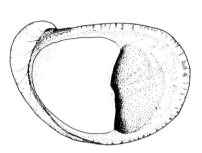

Crepidula fornicata (from below)

side view

Calyptraea chinensis

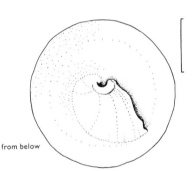

from below

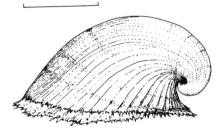

Capulus ungaricus

Aporrhais pes-pelecani (L.)

Height: 43 mm; *Breadth:* 31 mm.

Diagnostic characters: Shell prominently sculptured, with, in the adult, prominent expansion of the outer lip of the aperture to form a digitated structure resembling a pelican's foot.

Habitat: On muddy substrates off-shore; widely distributed, except extreme south-west.

General features: Like several interesting marine sea-shells, *Aporrhais* inhabits the sea bed in deeper waters and only reaches the shore when washed up as an empty shell. In a similar category, but with a quite different habitat, is the snail, *Ianthina janthina* (L.). Its globular (20 mm), violet-coloured shell might be found stranded on western coasts facing the Atlantic during the summer. Unlike the normal, bottom-living snails, *Ianthina* floats in the surface waters of the sea, suspended by a bubbly raft of mucus produced by the foot, and it feeds on the similarly drifting coelenterate (siphonophore), *Velella*.

Natica alderi Forbes [*N. poliana* Chiaje]

Height: 14 mm; *Breadth:* 13 mm.

Diagnostic characters: Shell smooth and globular, buff-coloured with spiral rows of reddish-brown spots or streaks, five on the body whorl; 6 whorls, only short spire; prominent umbilicus partly occluded at the top by a hard pad; large, plough-shaped foot covers head and front of shell; sand-studded jelly mass containing eggs resembles a necklace or collar.

Habitat: Animal burrows in sand, but also empty shells seen on surface; low-water mark and below, widely distributed.

General features: *Natica* is a sand-burrowing carnivorous snail which uses its large foot for ploughing beneath the surface. It adopts a digging technique similar to that employed by the bivalve molluscs, on which it in fact feeds after drilling a neat, round hole in the shell.

Natica catena (da Costa)

Height: 32 mm; *Breadth:* 30 mm.

Diagnostic characters: Similar in general form and habit to *N. alderi* but much larger; shell buff-coloured with one spiral row of reddish-brown streaks on upper surface of each whorl; 7 whorls and a short spire; large umbilicus, not occluded at top by a pad.

Habitat: In sandy bays, at low water and off-shore.

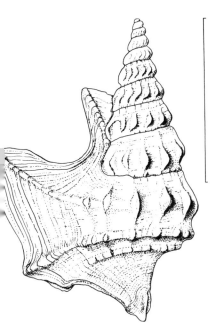

Aporrhais pes-pelecani

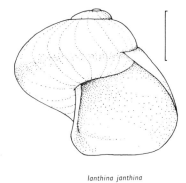

Ianthina janthina

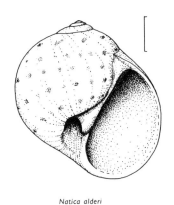

Natica alderi

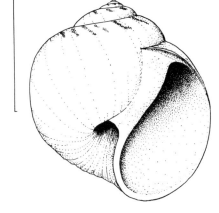

Natica catena

Trivia monacha (da Costa)

Height: 10 mm; *Breadth:* 13 mm.

Diagnostic characters: Shell in which the body whorl envelopes the other whorls producing a characteristic shape with slit-like aperture; glossy-white, finely-ribbed shell with three purple-brown spots; shell covered in living animal by a brightly-coloured mantle.

Habitat: Under rocks and boulders, low-water mark (*Laminaria* zone) and below; widely distributed, but perhaps more likely to be found in the south and west.

General features: Trivia is the only British representative of the cowries, which with their large, glossy and beautifully coloured shells are abundant on tropical coasts. The highly glazed surface results from the shell being protected during growth by the mantle tissues. *Trivia* feeds on compound sea-squirts, in the tissues of which it deposits egg-capsules, stalked and vase-shaped, during the breeding season. The very similar *T. arctica* (Montagu), also generally distributed but more frequent off-shore, is distinguished by its slightly smaller, unspotted shell.

Lamellaria perspicua (L.)

Length (animal): 20 mm (on shore); *Shell:* 14 × 10 mm.

Diagnostic characters: Shell white, internally enclosed, $2\frac{1}{2}$–3 whorls, reduced spire; body mottled yellow; one pair of tentacles, siphon behind head; head hidden below body.

Habitat: Under stones, lower shore downwards, usually associated with encrusting compound sea-squirts, on which it feeds; generally distributed.

General features: This slug-like mollusc is not to be confused with the true sea slugs (see pp. 66 to 74) from which it differs in many ways, for example, in bearing one and not two pairs of tentacles. *Lamellaria* is more closely related to the periwinkles and cowries, continuing the tendency, recurrent throughout the gastropods, and shown above by *Trivia*, to overgrow and reduce the shell. In the related *Velutina velutina* (Müller), the characteristic velvety-brown boat-shaped shell is much more prominent and only partly enclosed by the mantle tissues; the empty shell may be found on the beach.

Trivia monacha

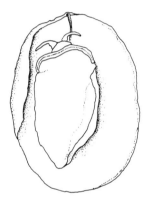

Lamellaria perspicua (ventral view)

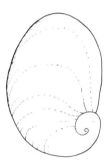

L. perspicua—shell

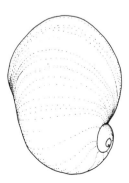

Velutina velutina

Nucella lapillus (L.)   Dog whelk

Height: 32 mm; *Breadth:* 20 mm.

Diagnostic characters: Shell thick and strong, with spirally ridged surface; short and conical; off-white or yellowish, but may be banded with darker colours; aperture relatively small with thick white lip on outer aspect, gently ridged internally and with a short, deep notch (siphonal canal) at the base.

Habitat: Abundant on all rocky shores, especially associated with barnacles, and also common on mussel beds; vase-shaped egg-capsules common on undersurface of rocks.

General features: Nucella is one of the most successful members of the neogastropod group of marine snails popularly known as whelks, all with carnivorous habits. They obtain food via an extensible proboscis through which the radula is extruded to rasp the tissues of the prey. Since the latter are normally hard-shelled, e.g. bivalves or crustaceans, the whelk has often to gain entry by drilling a hole through the shell by means of the radula. Whelks are also characterised by possession of a siphon (p. 19), a tube-like extension of the mantle edge which protrudes through the characteristic siphonal notch in the aperture of the strongly built shell (fig. 4). The dog whelk is one of the commonest carnivorous mulluscs on rocky shores, the pale shelled forms said to be feeding chiefly on barnacles, and the darker or banded varieties on mussels. Species of the related whelk, *Trophon*, distinguished by a more turreted shell and larger siphonal canal, are much rarer and confined to deeper waters.

Ocenebra erinacea (L.)

Height: 30 mm; *Breadth:* 17 mm.

Diagnostic characters: Shell with very prominent sculpture, waved longitudinal ribs and complex spiral ridges giving strong, rugged appearance; 8–10 angular whorls with well-marked suture; yellow-white; siphonal canal closed in mature specimens, but open in young.

Habitat: Low-water mark, but more abundant off-shore, where it feeds on bivalves, including oysters; mainly south and west coasts, also Wales and Ireland, rare in north.

General features: This species can attack oysters, but the related introduced American whelk-tingle or oyster-drill, *Urosalpinx cinerea* (Say), with a similar but less rugose shell and an open siphonal canal, is a serious and much more destructive pest of oyster beds. It is, however, limited to the coasts of Essex and Kent.

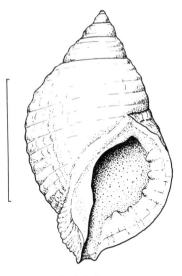

Nucella lapillus

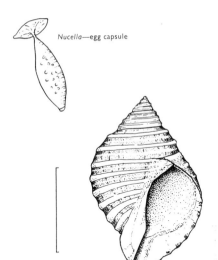

Nucella—egg capsule

N. lapillus—young banded specimen

Urosalpinx cinerea

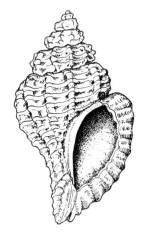

Ocenebra erinacea

Buccinum undatum (L.)   Common whelk

Height: 105 mm; *Breadth:* 65 mm.

Diagnostic characters: Shell large and solid, rather variable shape but typically with 7–8 whorls with wavy, wrinkled surface crossed by prominent growth lines and separated by deep suture; yellowish-white; aperture large, ovoid with short, wide siphonal canal; animal pale with black flecks.

Habitat: Widely distributed, lower shore downwards, on sandy or muddy bottom, larger specimens being found in deeper water; small intertidal forms favour muddy areas between rocks and stones.

General features: This is one of the best known and largest whelks, commoner off-shore, and noted of course for the palatable flesh. It attacks living bivalves by holding the valves open with the edge of its own shell before inserting the proboscis, but it also feeds on moribund or freshly killed animals. The latter habit is used to capture *Buccinum* by enticing it into wicker pots baited with recently killed crabs or fish. The common whelk is fished commercially at a number of places, including Grimsby, certain parts of East Anglia, and around Whitstable, over 2,000,000 kg being taken annually. It is perhaps regarded as less of a delicacy now than it was in previous centuries, but it is still an important consumable commodity. The closely related, large (150 mm) *Neptunea antiqua* (L.), distinguished by a more spindle-shaped shell with a smoother, spirally ridged surface, and an aperture, sometimes orange tinged internally, with an elongated siphonal canal, is found off northern coasts. It is also edible and may be captured in whelk pots along with *Buccinum*. Even more spindle-shaped with a smaller aperture and shallower suture is *Colus gracilis* (da Costa), another large species (65 mm) taken in northern waters, but not normally used for food. All the large whelks, because of their size, provide suitable homes as empty shells for fully-grown hermit crabs, which when younger inhabit the smaller shells of other marine snails. They are also favourite resting places for sea-anemones. The *Buccinum* shell, for example, appears particularly attractive to the sea-anemone, *Calliactis*, which attaches itself to the shell surface, thereby establishing with tenanted shells a mutual association with the hermit crab living inside.

½ nat.
size

Buccinum undatum

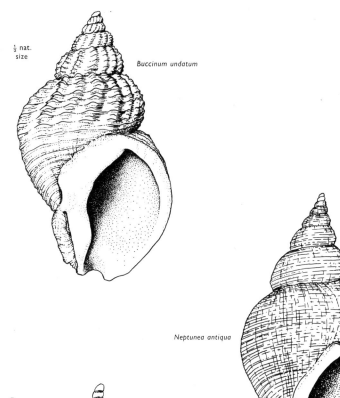

½ nat.
size

Neptunea antiqua

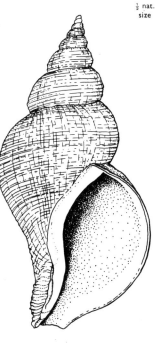

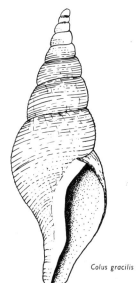

Colus gracilis

Nassarius reticulatus (L.)

Height: 28 mm; *Breadth:* 14 mm.

Diagnostic characters: Shell relatively smaller than other whelks described, with prominent spire of ten whorls; net-like sculpture caused by criss-crossing of longitudinal ribs and spiral ridges; brown or greenish-grey; outer lip of aperture bears tooth-like processes on inner margin.

Habitat: On rocky shores, widely distributed; a very active scavenger in areas of muddy sand, rich in organic material; lower reaches of shore and off-shore.

Nassarius incrassatus (Ström)

Height: 12 mm; *Breadth:* 6 mm.

Diagnostic characters: Shell similar to *N. reticulatus* but smaller and with characteristic brown blotch at the base; 8–9 whorls, more obvious and separated by more clearly defined suture; well marked longitudinal ribs; variably coloured but often with reddish-brown bands.

Habitat: Widely distributed on rocky shores, mainly under stones and in crevices, but in less silted areas (contrast *N. reticulatus*); lower shore and below. Other small carnivorous whelks include species of *Mangelia* and *Philbertia* with elongated, turreted, spindly shells lacking an operculum, found more typically in off-shore waters.

Acteon tornatilis (L.)

Height: 22 mm; *Breadth:* 11 mm.

Diagnostic characters: Shell oval or barrel-shaped, 7 whorls; pink or brown with 3 white bands; long aperture into which the animal can withdraw completely; operculum present.

Habitat: In sand, lower shore downwards; usually buried but empty shells may be washed up on beach; widely distributed.

General features: This species introduces the opisthobranch snails, i.e. gastropods which have lateral or posterior gills and tend to lose the shell. In primitive forms (sometimes known as 'tectibranchs') the shell is retained. *Acteon* represents an early condition with an operculum and with a shell which is still well developed and external. A related off-shore form also with a prominent shell only partly covered but lacking an operculum is *Tricla lignaria* (L.) an active predator with a large canoe-shaped shell.

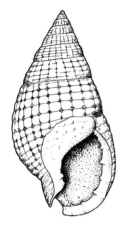

Nassarius reticulatus

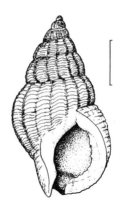

Nassarius incrassatus

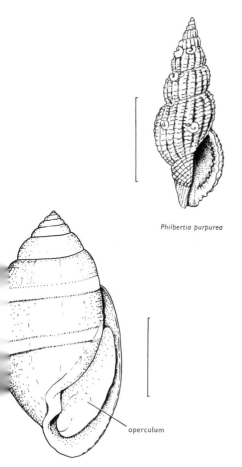

Philbertia purpurea

operculum

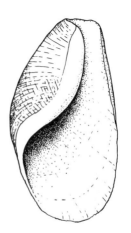

Tricla lignaria

Akera bullata Müller

Length (animal): 46 mm; *Height* (shell): 14 mm; *Breadth* (shell): 9 mm.

Diagnostic characters: Shell pale, thin, rather elastic; coiled with reduced spire, aperture extends whole length of shell; no operculum; body of animal normally envelopes shell; well developed lateral processes of foot (parapodia).

Habitat: On tidal mud flats, or on beds of *Zostera* (eel-grass); widely but locally distributed.

General features: The shell of *Akera* is still external but more encompassed by the body than in *Acteon* or *Tricla*. The parapodia, flaplike extensions of the foot, are prominent and used for active swimming, especially in the breeding season. These and all subsequent opisthobranchs which are practically devoid of a protective shell need to be observed in water in order to appreciate fully the delicate body structure. Other somewhat similar forms, retaining an external, although often almost covered shell, include species of *Haminoea*, with a shell bearing a reduced spire and elongated aperture, found locally on mud-flats or muddy gravel, and *Retusa*, with a tiny (4 mm) white shell, on muddy or sandy ground.

Turbonilla elegantissima (Montagu)

Height: 8 mm; *Breadth:* 2 mm.

Diagnostic characters: Shell small, constituting an elongated cone, slender but well built; white; up to 25 obliquely curved ribs.

Habitat: In silt or sand at low water associated with sedentary burrowing worms, eg. *Amphitrite*; widely distributed, but more frequent in the south-west.

General features: This small, elongate gastropod is one of a very large family of almost forty species, the pyramidellids, less well known because of their size and the ectoparasitic associations which they form with worms, echinoderms and, indeed, other molluscs. Recent work has demonstrated their allegiance to the opisthobranchs, rather than to the prosobranch gastropods. *Turbonilla*, like other members of the family, uses a proboscis to suck blood from the host tissues. Species of the related genus, *Odostomia*, may parasitise tubed worms, eg. *Pomatoceros*, and bivalves, including the commercially important scallops, mussels and oysters. In the latter case, the tiny snail inhabits the edge of the shell feeding on the marginal tissues of the mantle.

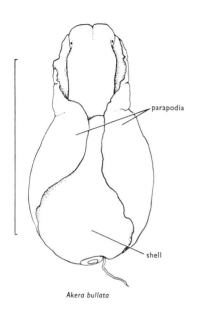

parapodia

shell

Akera bullata

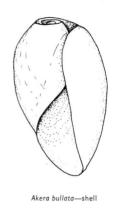

Akera bullata—shell

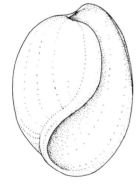

Haminoea navicula

Turbonilla elegantissima

Philine quadripartita Ascanius

Length (animal): 40 mm; *Height* (shell): 14 mm; *Breadth* (shell): 12 mm.

Diagnostic characters: Shell, delicate, white, completely enclosed by the white body which is divided into 4 lobes, one anterior head shield, two lateral (parapodial) lobes, and one posterior (mantle) lobe.

Habitat: Sandy substrates, mainly off-shore and only very occasionally washed up; widely distributed.

General features: This is one of the commonest of several opisthobranchs demonstrating complete enclosure with further reduction of the shell, and showing a progressive tendency towards a slug-like form. In the not unrelated, tiny (5 mm long) *Pelta coronata* (Quatrefages), a dark slug-like mollusc, frequently found on shore in rock pools, the shell has been lost completely.

Reference might be made at this point to the Pteropoda or 'sea-butterflies', a group of opisthobranch molluscs which are microscopic forms, members of the plankton, i.e. drifting life in the surface waters of the sea. They use the wing-like parapodia, so characteristic of many shore members of this group, for swimming in the sea. Some forms like *Spiratella* are shelled, others (e.g. *Clione*) are naked.

Aplysia punctata Cuvier   Sea hare

Length (animal): 120 mm.

Diagnostic characters: Shell reduced, translucent, horny, internally enclosed by mantle; brown to olive-green as adult, reddish when young, both spotted; as in many opisthobranchs, two pairs of tentacles, anterior (cephalic) and posterior (rhinophores); rear end of foot prolonged and pointed; parapodia extend to dorsal surface.

Habitat: Mainly off-shore in *Laminaria*, but comes nearer low water in spring to lay coils of pinkish eggs around seaweed; found quite frequently in *Zostera* beds; widely distributed, locally but irregularly common.

General features: Aplysia, the so-called 'sea-hare' because of the shape of its posterior (upper) pair of tentacles, crawls using the large foot or swims actively by means of the parapodia. The shell is still present but is enclosed by the body and not visible from the exterior. Unlike many other opisthobranchs, *Aplysia* is herbivorous, feeding on seaweeds. When disturbed it emits a characteristic purple slime.

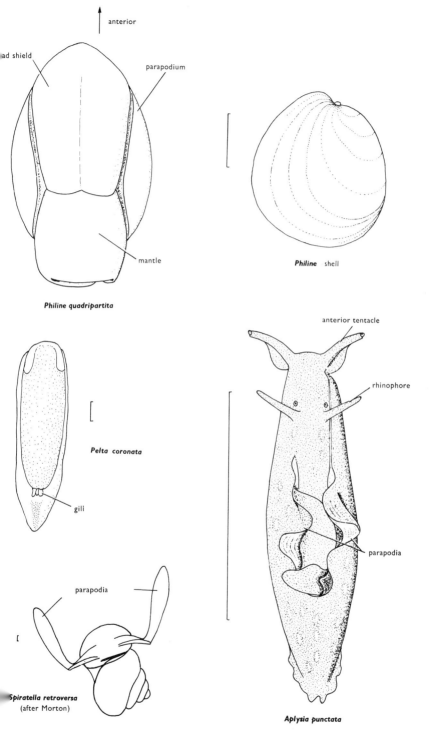

anterior

ad shield

parapodium

mantle

Philine quadripartita

Philine shell

Pelta coronata

gill

parapodia

Spiratella retroversa
(after Morton)

anterior tentacle

rhinophore

parapodia

Aplysia punctata

Elysia viridis (Montagu)

Length: 7 mm.

Diagnostic characters: Body greenish, bearing lateral, flattened lobes with paler margins; no dorsal processes or gills.

Habitat: Mainly associated with green seaweeds (e.g. *Codium*), in pools on rocky shores; more frequent on south and west coasts.

General features: This is one of a group of tiny sea-slugs which typically feed on green algae, sucking the juices from the plant tissues after penetrating them with the radula. Others with similar habits are *Acteonia senestra* (Quatrefages), also greenish and found in rock pools but lacking the lateral lobes characteristic of *Elysia*, *Limapontia* (2 species, one, *L. capitata* (Müller), a minute, 3 mm long, blackish slug, which occurs in pools on green filamentous weed), and *Alderia modesta* (Lovén), mottled yellowish-brown, with processes (cerata) down each side of the body, found locally in salt marshes.

Berthella plumula (Montagu)

Length: 40 mm.

Diagnostic characters: Body ovoid, light yellow enclosing thin white internal shell; feathery gill, free at the tip, on right-hand side; no parapodia.

Habitat: Lower shore, under rocks or in rock pools, feeding on sea-squirts; widely distributed.

Pleurobranchus membranaceus (Montagu)

Length: 85 mm.

Diagnostic characters: Shell enclosed, thin and membranous; body oval, substantial but fleshy; pale yellow with tuberculated reddish-brown back; generally similar in form to *Berthella* (above).

Habitat: Mainly in deeper water, but comes nearer shore during summer; sometimes appears in large swarms; generally but locally distributed.

General features: Since the flimsy internal shell in this opisthobranch has little structural value, the animal has to adopt other protective measures. In common with several other naked gastropods, *Pleurobranchus* produces strong acid secretions from its mantle and foot which act as an effective warning or deterrent to would-be attackers, including predatory fish. In some cases the mollusc is rejected only after it has been taken into the fish's mouth and is apparently unharmed by the experience.

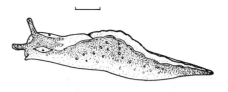

Elysia viridis (after Alder and Hancock)

Alderia modesta
(after Alder and Hancock)

Limapontia capitata

gill

Berthella plumula

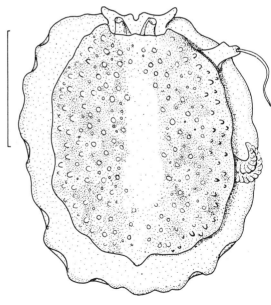

Pleurobranchus membranaceus

Archidoris pseudoargus (Rapp)

Length: 70 mm.

Diagnostic characters: Body tough, elliptical, yellowish; upper side is tubercled, blotched with brown or green; no shell; circlet around the anus of 9 tripinnate gills which are retractile, i.e. can be withdrawn into a cavity in the mantle; rhinophores complex with lateral folds; egg ribbons white and coiled.

Habitat: Common on rocky shores, usually associated with encrusting sponges, e.g. *Halichondria*, on which it feeds; widely distributed.

General features: This and the following group of species constitute the true sea-slugs or nudibranchs, often delicately frilled and beautifully coloured, which lack a shell completely. In a sense, however, this frees the upper surface of the body to take on many varied functions, including protection and camouflage, for sensory purposes and for respiration. The sensitive rhinophores are prominent and laminated. The large, lemon coloured *Archidoris pseudoargus* is one of the best known British nudibranchs. A red variety of this species (*var. flammea*) may also be found on shore, the colour deriving apparently from the red sponges on which it feeds, rather than the yellowish-white *Halichondria*. There is also, however, a quite distinct species not infrequently found, but only on S.W. shores, *A. stellifera* (Vayassière), mottled brown and yellow and with only 8 gills.

Cadlina laevis (L.)

Length: 25 mm.

Diagnostic characters: Animal white with tiny opaque white tubercles on back; yellowish spots on side of body; 5 small gills.

Habitat: Under rocks or in pools; north-east coasts.

Jorunna tomentosa (Cuvier)

Length: 45 mm.

Diagnostic characters: Resembles *Archidoris* in general shape but with smoother mantle and bears 11–15 white retractile gills; pale yellow with sparse brownish spots.

Habitat: Widely distributed but not frequent, on lower shore; also off-shore on gravel.

General features: This dorid in common with most nudibranchs is carnivorous, in this case, like the sea lemon, feeding on *Halichondria*. The related *Rostanga rufescens* (Iredale & O'Donoghue) is much smaller (12 mm) and distinguished by an orange-red mantle, black spotted, and ten small gills; it occurs largely on southern coasts, typically on red sponges.

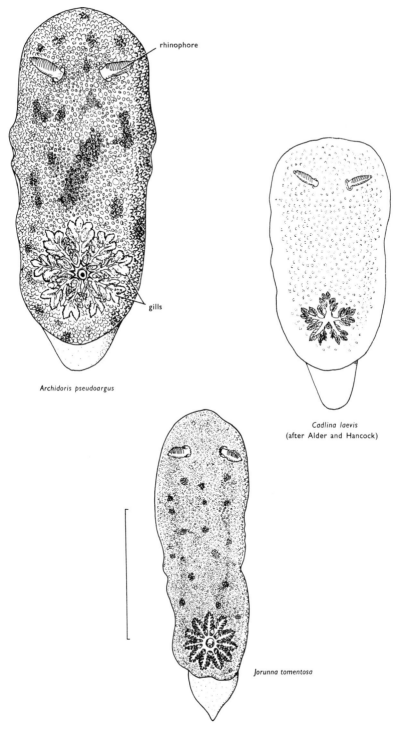

rhinophore

gills

Archidoris pseudoargus

Cadlina laevis
(after Alder and Hancock)

Jorunna tomentosa

Onchidoris fusca (Müller)

Length: 25 mm.

Diagnostic characters: Similar in general form to *Archidoris* but the mantle surface bears short, plump tubercles, is pale with mottled brown markings, and there are over 20 small, plumed gills (actual number variable), which are non-retractile; they form a circle around the anus incomplete at the rear.

Habitat: On shores associated with barnacles, also with the sea-mat, *Alcyonidium*, on which it feeds; widely distributed.

General features: This is one of the commonest of several species of *Onchidoris*, resembling the sea-lemon, but smaller and with gills that are non-retractile, i.e. cannot be withdrawn into a cavity in the mantle. Smaller still (8 mm long) is *O. muricata* (Müller), whitish in colour, with only 11 tiny gills, which is found more frequently on northern coasts, usually feeding on the encrusting sea-mats. An interesting diagnostic characteristic is that the skin of *O. fusca* produces a very acid secretion (see *Pleurobranchus*, p. 64) at pH 1–2, whereas the skin of other *Onchidoris* species is near neutrality.* Worth mentioning here is the related *Adalaria proxima* (Alder and Hancock), 12 mm long and yellowish-orange in colour (occasionally paler), also with 11 gills, but these are differentiated into 9 larger and 2 smaller plumes, lying some distance from the anus.

Length: 25 mm.

Diagnostic characters: Body transparent, incompletely covered by the wavy-edged mantle, which has an indentation posteriorly; whitish, tinged with pink; keel or ridge down back; 13 large, non-retractile, branched gills.

Habitat: Widely distributed on rocky shores, between tide-marks, under stones or in pools; feeds on ascidians (sea-squirts) and the encrusting bryozoans (sea-mats).

General features: This dorid is distinguished by, amongst other features, the incomplete nature of the mantle cloak. Similar, but less frequently found, is *G. castanea* Alder and Hancock, distinguished by a reddish-brown body and only 7–9 gills. Another form related to *Goniodoris* is *Ancula cristata* (Alder), small (12 mm), with a whitish body, and characterised by a ring of ten processes tipped with yellow surrounding three large gills.

*Information kindly provided by Dr. T. E. Thompson.

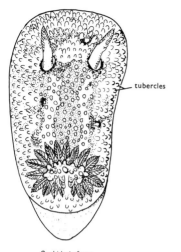

Onchidoris fusca
(after Alder and Hancock)

tubercles

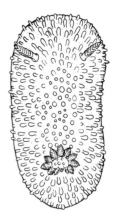

Onchidoris muricata
(after Alder and Hancock)

mantle

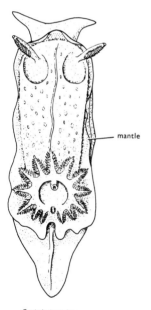

Goniodoris nodosa

Goniodoris castanea
(after Alder and Hancock)

Ancula cristata
(after Alder and Hancock)

Acanthodoris pilosa (Abildgaard)

Length: 25 mm.

Diagnostic characters: Body oval, markedly convex mantle with tall, pointed, soft-looking tubercles; variably coloured, white to purplish-brown; tips of tentacles point towards rear; ring of nine prominent feathery gills.

Habitat: Similarly distributed to *Goniodoris*, feeding on sea-mats.

Polycera quadrilineata (Müller)

Length: 15 mm.

Diagnostic characters: Body white with lines of yellow spots on each side; additional processes on head, and two behind the gills laterally, all, with the tentacles, yellow-tipped; 7–9 gills also tipped with yellow.

Habitat: Widely distributed, in shallow pools or on weeds, including *Zostera*, between tidemarks, or on *Laminaria*, associated with hydroids or sea-mats; also off-shore (*P. dubia* M. Sars, with only 3 gills and a yellowish-green body has similar habits, but found mainly on north-east coasts).

Limacia clavigera (Müller)

Length: 15 mm.

Diagnostic characters: Body small, whitish and flattened; 20 processes around margin of body tipped deep yellow; similarly coloured tubercles on back; three elongated gills.

Habitat: Widely distributed but not frequent; most likely to be seen during May and June associated with sea-mats at low water.

Dendronotus frondosus (Ascanius)

Length: 25 mm.

Diagnostic characters: Body yellowish, variously mottled, and distinguished by 6–7 very branched, arborescent processes (cerata) down each side of the back; rhinophores can be withdrawn into sheaths in mantle.

Habitat: At low water, but mainly off-shore, on weed or hydroid colonies; generally distributed.

General features: This nudibranch with its remarkable branched dorsal outgrowths, probably both respiratory and sensory in function, is one of a group of quite primitive sea-slugs. The related *Tritonia hombergi* Cuvier, the largest British nudibranch, bears 11–12 pairs of these processes, but is mainly a deeper water species.

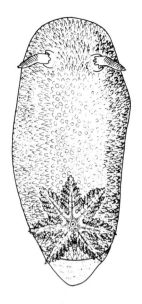

Acanthodoris pilosa

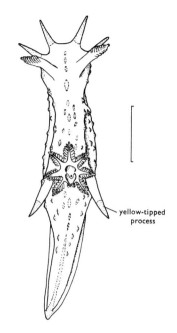

yellow-tipped process

Polycera quadrilineata
(after Alder and Hancock)

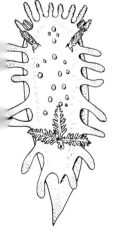

Limacia clavigera

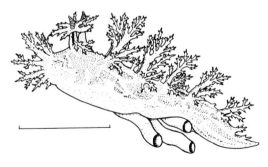

Dendronotus frondosus (after Alder and Hancock)

Aeolidia papillosa (L.)

Length: up to 75 mm.

Diagnostic characters: Body almost covered, except in the mid-line anteriorly, by numerous greyish-brown processes (cerata—see below), giving felt-like appearance to upper surface; anus lateral.

Habitat: On rocky shores, in pools amongst algae or on underside of rocks; common, widely distributed.

General features: This and related nudibranchs are characterised by the conspicuous processes or cerata on the upper surface of the body, which help in respiration. However, these apparently delicate and harmless structures also contain large numbers of stinging cells (nematocysts) which they obtain from coelenterates, e.g. hydroids and sea-anemones on which they feed. The nematocysts are transferred undamaged to the cerata where they act as deterrents to fish and other potential attackers. Some nudibranchs of this type flaunt their effective defence mechanism with bright colours to warn off possible aggressors; others, like *Aeolidia*, use the cerata as camouflage, in this case resembling the tentacles of the sea-anemones, e.g. *Anemonia sulcata*, on which they feed and near which they are commonly found. Related forms include species of *Coryphella*, occurring more frequently off-shore, in which the cerata are fewer in number and shorter than in *Aeolidia*, probably a primitive feature. Species of *Trinchesia* have fewer cerata still, often arranged in transverse rows; *T. aurantia* (Alder & Hancock), 10–12 mm long, with a pale brownish body and characteristic orange tipped cerata, is not uncommon both at extreme low water on hydroids, as well as off-shore. In the tiny, whitish, *Tergipes despectus* (Johnston), 5–6 mm long, there are only two rows of four large cerata arranged alternately along each side; it lives amongst hydroid colonies in the *Laminaria* zone.

Facelina auriculata (Müller)

Length: 25 mm.

Diagnostic characters: Body generally similar to *Aeolidia*, but smaller and more delicately coloured; slender and tapers posteriorly; cerata in 4–6 clusters, red and white tipped, but also giving characteristic bluish lustre; yellow rings on posterior tentacles.

Habitat: On rocky shores, amongst algae, and on the hydroid, *Tubularia;* generally distributed.

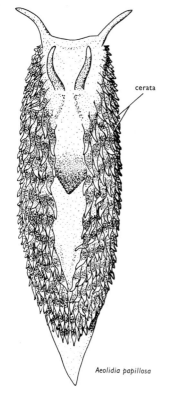

cerata

Aeolidia papillosa

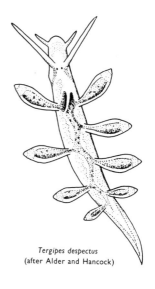

Tergipes despectus
(after Alder and Hancock)

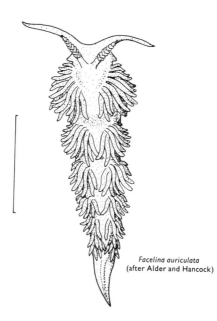

Facelina auriculata
(after Alder and Hancock)

Doto coronata (Gmelin)

Length: 12 mm.

Diagnostic characters: Body small, pale, with reddish or purple spots; cerata arranged in 5–7 pairs, large and club-shaped, giving top-heavy appearance to the animal.

Habitat: On shores, usually well hidden in fucoid seaweeds, amongst the hydroid colonies on which it feeds; widely distributed.

General features: This is one of four British species of this beautiful nudibranch. *D. fragilis* (Forbes), more evenly and darker coloured, is also quite frequently found. Mention might also be made here of *Janolus cristatus* (Chiaje), a much larger form (40 mm), found mainly in the south and west, which is characterised by prominent lateral rows of cerata arranged, like an aeolid, with lustrous white tips.

Phytia myosotis (Draparnaud) (N.B. Pulmonata)

Height: 7 mm; Breadth: 3 .mm.

Diagnostic characters: Shell small, thin, spindle-shaped with pointed spire; pale brown; up to three tooth-like ridges on inner (columellar) side of aperture, outer lip usually smooth; no operculum.

Habitat: On mud-flats, estuaries and salt-marshes, amongst vegetation, or rubbish; fairly generally distributed.

General features: This small snail is one of the few shore pulmonates, nevertheless, a primitive member of this group which so dominates the land and freshwater molluscan fauna. Smaller still (4 mm) and narrower is the rather strong, whitish shell of *Leucophytia bidentata* (Montagu), with only two ridges on the inner lip of the aperture; this pulmonate is less widely distributed (mainly south and west) and found near high water hidden in crevices or beneath stones. In similar localities and in empty barnacle shells (especially of *Chthamalus stellatus*) on the upper shore one might find the minute *Otina ovata* (Brown), with a tiny (2 mm) ear-shaped shell of barely more than two whorls, the body whorl being very large but unable to contain the animal completely. Worth mentioning here also is the small (12 mm long) and slug-like *Onchidella celtica* Forbes and Hanley. This greyish-black animal, considered by some authorities to be an opisthobranch, has no shell but is provided with a thick protective mantle studded with tubercles; it lives in rock crevices on the upper shore, but limited to the south-west.

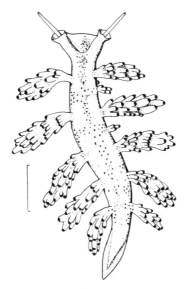

Doto coronata
(after Alder and Hancock)

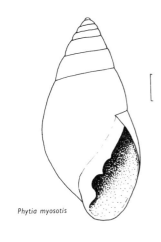

Phytia myosotis

Leucophytia bidentata

Otina ovata

Key to Freshwater and Brackish-Water Gastropoda

Note: Bracketed sizes in this key indicate shell height.

1. Operculum present; one pair of tentacles; respiration by gills   2
   Operculum absent; two pairs of tentacles; respiration usually
   by means of a lung   9

2. Thick shell with small spire; mottled pattern, aperture semi-
   circular   ..   ..   *Theodoxus fluviatilis* (p. 80)
   Thinner shell with taller spire; usually without mottled
   pattern; aperture rounder   3

3. Large shell usually over 30 mm tall, often with brown bands   4
   Shell smaller, under 15 mm high, rarely banded   5

4. Suture relatively shallow; aperture rather oval; umbilicus
   ill-defined   ..   ..   ..   *Viviparus viviparus* (p. 84)
   Suture deeper; whorls very swollen; aperature rounder;
   umbilicus distinct   ..   ..   *Viviparus contectus* (p. 84)

5. Shell only slightly taller than broad, or more flattened; gills
   protrude from beneath shell in active animal   6
   Shell considerably taller than broad, with obvious spire; gills
   not protruded in active animal   7

6. Shell flat and disc-like, very small, less than 4 mm broad
        Valvata cristata (p. 84)
   Shell almost as tall as it is broad, somewhat larger (about 5 mm
   across)   ..   ..   *Valvata piscinalis* (p. 84)

7. Operculum limy; height commonly greater than 6–10 mm; in
   freshwater   ..   ..   *Bithynia* spp. (p. 80)
   Operculum horny; height usually less than 6–10 mm; shell
   elongate and rather narrow; in brackish or fresh water   ..   8

8. Whorls flattened, shallow suture; top of aperture pointed; brackish-water, common on mud flats   *Hydrobia ulvae* (p. 82)
   Whorls rounded (large body whorl), deeper suture; top of aperture rounded; in brackish or more especially fresh water
   Potamopyrgus jenkinsi (p. 82)

9. Shell limpet like   10
   Shell not limpet-like; coiled or helically wound   11

10. Shell with arched apex, median or slightly inclined to the right   ..   ..   *Ancylus fluviatilis* (p. 94)
    Shell flatter and narrower, apex turned to the left
    Acroloxus [*Ancylus*] *lacustris* (p. 94)

11. Shell globular or conical, helically wound with spire; taller than broad   12
    Shell disc-like, coiled mainly in one plane; broader than tall (Planorbidae: Ramshorn snails)   18

12. Shell sinistral, i.e. aperture to the left; shell thin with swollen body whorl and tall aperture   ..   ..   *Physa fontinalis* (p. 88)
    Shell dextral, i.e. aperture to the right   13

13. Shell very thin pale amber; body whorl and aperture very large, latter pointed above; eyes on tip of tentacles; on water plants, seldom submerged   ..   ..   ..   *Succinea* spp.
    (described with terrestrial gastropods; see p. 104)
    Shell generally thicker; aperture otherwise-shaped; eyes on swelling at base of tentacles; usually submerged in water (Lymnaeidea: Pond snails)   14

14 Shell large (45 mm), with elongate and acute spire ..   ..
   Lymnaea stagnalis (p. 86)
   Smaller shell (25 mm or less), spire less acute   15

15. Shell with tall spire, height of which is similar to or slightly
    greater than that of the aperture   16
    Shell with short spire, much less tall than the height of the
    aperture   17

16. Small snail (8 mm high), rather slim, usually light brown, can
    live mainly out of water   ..   *Lymnaea truncatula* (p. 86)
    Medium sized snail (15 mm), darkish-coloured, rather thick
    shell   ..   ..   *Lymnaea palustris* (p. 86)

17. Last (body) whorl expanded into large ear-shaped aperture,
    upper edge of which meets body at right angle   ..   ..
                            Lymnaea auricularia (p. 88)
    Body whorl less expanded; upper edge of aperture usually
    meets body at less than a right angle   *Lymnaea peregra* (p. 88)

18. Large shell with total breadth of 25 mm or more   ..   ..
                            Planorbarius corneus (p. 90)
    Less broad   19

19. Shell with marked transverse ridges; very small, 2 mm across
                            Planorbis crista (p. 92)
    Shell surface smooth   20

20. Shell with 6–8 whorls   21
    Shell usually with smaller number of whorls   22

21. Closely coiled, narrow whorls forming thick, compact disc,
    6 mm across   ..   ..   ..   *Planorbis contortus* (p. 94)
    Broader, prominently keeled whorls forming very thin,
    flattened disc, 8 mm across, aperture twisted ..   ..   ..
                            Planorbis vortex (p. 92)
    Disc (6.5 mm) of less angular whorls; aperture bears white rib
                    Planorbis leucostoma [*P. spirorbis*] (p. 92)

22. Shell with overlapping whorls; appears lens-shaped with tapered edges in side view; small shell, only 3–4 mm across
Segmentina complanata (p. 94)

Shell otherwise shaped and larger; whorls less obviously overlapping   23

23. Shell off-white with rounded whorls, 5 mm across   ..   ..
Planorbis albus (p. 92)

Shell larger (14 mm broad) darker, with marginal keel   ..   24

24. Keel pronounced, towards middle of shell; oval aperture   ..
Planorbis carinatus (p. 90)

Keel less pronounced, towards one side of shell; aperture rounded   ..   ..   *Planorbis planorbis* (p. 90)

Theodoxus fluviatilis (L.)

Height: 6 mm; *Breadth:* 11 mm.

Diagnostic characters: Shell small, thick, globular, with shallow spire and large body whorl; colour variable, yellowish to brown with variegated darker markings; no umbilicus; semi-circular aperture; limy operculum.

Habitat: Favours hard water; in rivers or streams on stones and under bridges, or, less often, on plants; also wave-line in lakes; widely distributed in England, except Devon and Cornwall, central Ireland; Wales only in Glamorgan, Scotland only in Orkney.

General features: This and the next few species are fresh- and brackish-water representatives of the primitive (prosobranch) snails which so dominate the marine seashore scene. They show the same character-istics of breathing by means of a true gill and are operculate, i.e. they possess an operculum attached to the foot which closes the aperture of the shell when the body is withdrawn. *Theodoxus* is the only British freshwater member of the oldest (archaeo–) gastropods which have more successfully diversified, like the true limpets and their relatives, in their ancestral habitat, the sea.

Bithynia tentaculata (L.)

Height: 10 mm; *Breadth:* 6 mm.

Diagnostic characters: Shell strong, conical, 5–6 whorls, suture shallow; yellowish; umbilicus nearly closed; limy operculum.

Habitat: Favours hard water, quiet rivers and still water, but not small ponds; widely distributed; common.

General features: This species, in common with other hydrobiid snails described below, feeds using an elongated snout, and the head bears characteristic long, slender tentacles. The smaller (6 mm tall) *B. leachi* (Sheppard), with more rounded whorls and deeper suture, is less common and more locally distributed. Both species, like *Theodoxus* above, are calciphile, i.e. calcium-loving species, always found in hard water containing more than 20 mg calcium per litre. In common with several other snails favouring similar conditions, these species have strongly built, heavily calcified shells.

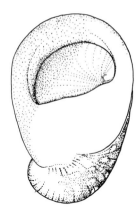

Theodoxus fluviatilis

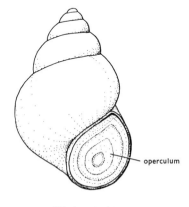

operculum

Bithynia tentaculata

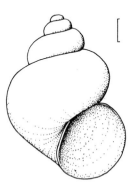

Bithynia leachi

Potamopyrgus jenkinsi (Smith)

Height: 5 mm; *Breadth:* 3 mm.

Diagnostic characters: Shell small, generally pointed, occasionally with raised spiral by arranged keel; 5–6 whorls, large body whorl; dark colour on yellowish background; umbilicus almost closed; horny operculum; top of aperture rounded.

Habitat: Brackish water (e.g. estuaries) and, more particularly, fresh water, where it is common in running water, rivers, streams, canals, etc.; widely distributed.

General features: Probably introduced into Britain in the nineteenth century and officially recorded in brackish-water in 1889, this species subsequently invaded freshwater habitats by the end of the century. It has since spread rapidly to fresh waters throughout the country where it is now abundant. *Potamopyrgus* is a viviparous snail and, more unusually, males are, except for one record, unknown. Development is therefore from the unfertilised egg, i.e. by parthenogenesis, a phenomenon which occurs quite frequently in certain invertebrate groups, e.g. insects, but is rare in molluscs.

Hydrobia [*Peringia or Sabanaea*] *ulvae* (Pennant)

Height: 6 mm; *Breadth:* 3 mm.

Diagnostic characters: Shell small, elongate, with up to six more flattened whorls; shallow suture; variably coloured; top of aperture pointed; very narrow umbilicus; horny operculum.

Habitat: Often associated with the sea-lettuce, *Ulva*, or on surface of mud, feeding on algae or detritus, in estuaries and salt marshes; it may be abundant on mud flats giving the surface a granular appearance; widely distributed.

General features: This is another common brackish-water snail, which, with *Potamopyrgus* above, belongs to the Hydrobiidae, a family probably quite closely related to the tiny marine rissoids (p. 44). The less frequent *Hydrobia ventrosa* (Montagu) is distinguished by a smaller (4 mm) shell with more rounded whorls separated by a deeper suture and with a rounder aperture. Other brackish-water snails include the small (4 mm), swollen shelled *Pseudamnicola confusa* (Frauenfeld), locally distributed, mainly in the S.E. and E., and the conical (5 mm), flat sided *Assiminea grayana* Fleming, found in the Thames estuary and along the east coast.

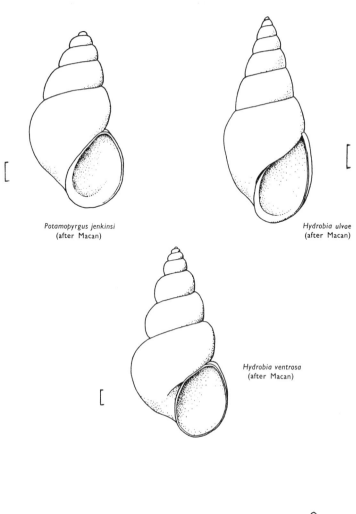

Potamopyrgus jenkinsi
(after Macan)

Hydrobia ulvae
(after Macan)

Hydrobia ventrosa
(after Macan)

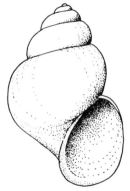

Pseudamnicola confusa

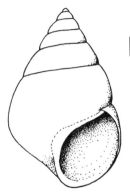

Assiminea grayana

Viviparus viviparus (L.)

Height: 40 mm; *Breadth:* 32 mm.

Diagnostic characters: Shell large, thick, usually banded with 3 dark bands on greenish-brown background; not glossy; 6–7 whorls; umbilicus very reduced; aperture oval; hard, horny operculum.

Habitat: Hard water, slow moving rivers and canals; England, as far north as Yorkshire, and Wales.

General features: This constitutes one of the largest and best known of the operculate type of freshwater snail. With the even larger introduced species, *V. japonicus* (Martens), it is a popular aquarium snail. Unusually amongst snails, *Viviparus* is a ciliary or filter feeder. It is viviparous and bears its young alive, some 50 at a time.

Viviparus contectus (Millet) [*V. fasciatus* Müller]

Height: 36 mm; *Breadth:* 30 mm.

Diagnostic characters: Shell thinner and shinier than *V. viviparus* with more pointed apex; 6–7 swollen whorls and deeper suture giving stair-case format to shell; umbilicus prominent; aperture rounder; hard, horny operculum.

Habitat: As above, north to Yorkshire, but more restricted and less common.

Valvata piscinalis (Müller)

Height: 6 mm; *Breadth:* 6 mm.

Diagnostic characters: Shell small, globular and shaped rather like a top; 4–4½ whorls, umbilicus deep but narrow; aperture almost circular; operculum; plumose gill and filament emerge from mantle cavity; long snout; foot deeply divided anteriorally.

Habitat: Soft water species which favours flowing water; widely distributed, but infrequent in northern Scotland.

Valvata cristata (Müller)

Height: 1 mm; *Breadth:* 3 mm.

Diagnostic characters: Shell very small, disc-like, but distinguished from similarly shaped planorbid snails (see pp. 90–92) by operculum and other special features designated above for *V. piscinalis*.

Habitat: Also tolerates soft water; in slow-flowing, muddy streams or stagnant waters, especially amongst dense plant growth; widely distributed, but not Cornwall and parts of Scotland.

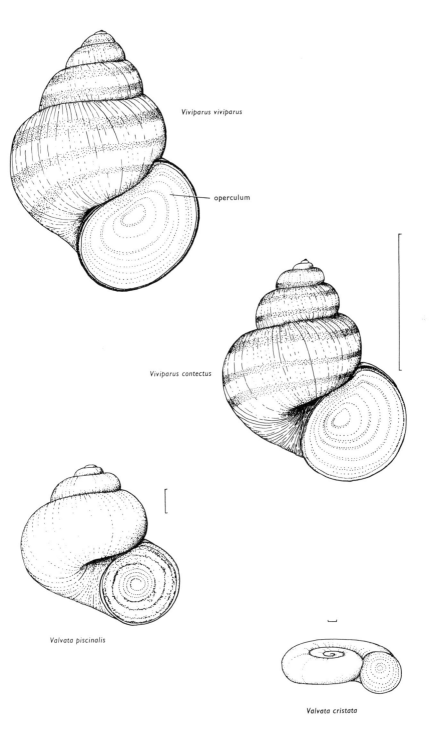

Viviparus viviparus

operculum

Viviparus contectus

Valvata piscinalis

Valvata cristata

Lymnaea stagnalis (L.)   Great pond snail

Height: 45 mm; *Breadth:* 25 mm.

Diagnostic characters: Shell large, thin, with narrow, tapering spire, 7–8 whorls, body whorl large comprising ¾ height of shell; pale to dark brown; umbilicus closed; no operculum.

Habitat: Favours hard water, slow moving or stagnant, including larger ponds; widely distributed and common in England, Wales, Ireland and parts of S. Scotland.

General features: This and the following species are non-operculate pulmonates, and share therefore a common ancestry with the air-breathing land snails (see p. 96). Although they may remain submerged in water for long periods, they usually have to return to the surface to renew the air supply in their lung-like mantle cavity. *L. stagnalis*, the largest member of the well known family Lymnaeidae (pond snails) is much more voracious than the other mainly herbivorous species, showing a partiality for dead, and even living, animal material, including newts and small fish.

Lymnaea truncatula (Müller)

Height: 8 mm; *Breadth:* 4 mm.

Diagnostic characters: Shell small, rather slim, 5–6 swollen whorls; light brown or horny shade; small open umbilicus.

Habitat: Widespread in marshy shallow waters, including flooded pastures; animals can live out of water in moist conditions.

General features: This snail is well known as the specific intermediate host of the liver fluke (*Fasciola hepatica*), found as adults in sheep. Its amphibious habit makes it ideally suited to this role. The taller (15 mm) cylindrical *L. glabra* (Müller) can also survive drier conditions; it occurs very locally in difficult habitats, for example, temporary ponds and ditches.

Lymnaea palustris (Müller)

Height: 19 mm; *Breadth:* 9 mm.

Diagnostic characters: Shell strong, elongated, spire tapered and approximately as tall as the aperture; 6–7 whorls; suture shallow; brown surface, spirally and transversely striated; no umbilicus.

Habitat: Inhabits marshy areas, like *L. truncatula*, but also in ponds, ditches and the edge of lakes; widely distributed, rarer in N.W. Scotland.

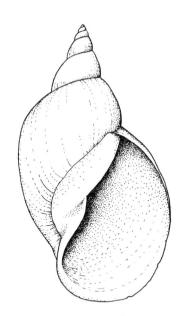

Lymnaea stagnalis

Lymnaea truncatula

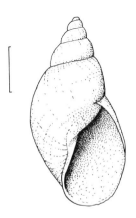

Lymnaea palustris

Lymnaea auricularia (L.)

Height: 22 mm; *Breadth:* 20 mm.

Diagnostic characters: Shell thin walled, broad, with characteristic large ear-shaped aperture, upper edge of which forms a right angle with the body whorl; short, sharply pointed spire; 4–5 whorls; glossy, pale brown; umbilicus small and slit-like or covered.

Habitat: Favours hard water; in canals, rivers, large ponds, lakes; widely distributed, except Cornwall (introduced) and northern Scotland.

Lymnaea peregra (Müller)

Height: 19 mm; *Breadth:* 13 mm.

Diagnostic characters: Shell usually thin with a less pointed spire, 4–5 whorls, but variably shaped (large number of named varieties); large body whorl; unlike *L. auricularia* above, upper edge of aperture usually makes a more acute angle with the body whorl; yellowish-brown; umbilicus almost covered.

Habitat: The commonest freshwater snail in the British Isles, found in almost all types of habitat; it withstands a wide range of environmental conditions and shows considerable variation in shell form relative to external factors; animals spawn twice a year, the jelly covered egg masses being attached to weeds, stones or other suitable substrates.

Physa fontinalis (L.)

Height: 10 mm; *Breadth:* 6 mm.

Diagnostic characters: Shell sinistral (coiled to left), very thin, glossy and brittle; 4–5 whorls, body whorl large and swollen; pale yellow-brown; tall aperture; in living animal the mantle edge is turned back over the shell.

Habitat: Widely distributed except Cornwall and northern Scotland, in moving water including clear streams, commonly on weeds; less frequently in lakes or large ponds (other species of *Physa* may be found both in natural and artificial habitats, but these are forms introduced from abroad); *Aplexa hypnorum* (L.) is another sinistral species, but with a more pointed shell (12 mm) bearing a smaller, narrower aperture; it is locally distributed in ponds and ditches; unlike *Physa*, the shell is not covered in the living animal by the mantle tissues.

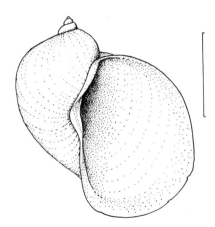

Lymnaea auricularia

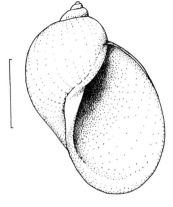

Lymnaea peregra

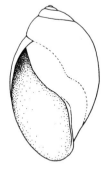

Physa fontinalis

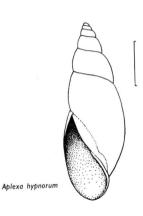

Aplexa hypnorum

Planorbarius [*Planorbis*] *corneus* (L.)   Great Ramshorn Snail

Height: 10 mm; *Breadth:* 25 mm.

Diagnostic characters: Shell large, thick-walled, coiled in a flat spiral to form a thick disc; 5–6 rounded whorls; glossy, dark brown surface; animal brown to red.

Habitat: Lives in hard water, both moving or stagnant, including lakes, canals, rivers, ponds, rich in vegetation; England, mainly south-eastern, and Wales (except west), rather locally distributed; local in Ireland.

General features: This is the largest member of the family Planorbidae, popularly known as Ramshorn snails. They have a characteristic shell, actually sinistral, wound in one plane to form a flattened disc. Planorbids are more fully adapted to life in water than the pond snails, part of the mantle being modified as a secondary gill. They are true herbivores, always requiring water weeds or other vegetation for food, and often therefore in life associated with such vegetation. Unlike most molluscs, *Planorbis* has red blood containing the pigment haemoglobin. This aids in respiration and may provide a temporary store of oxygen when available supplies are poor.

Planorbis planorbis (L.)

Height: 3 mm; *Breadth:* 14 mm.

Diagnostic characters: Shell thick walled with small raised ridge (keel) towards one side; 5–6 rather narrow whorls; surface dull, yellow-brown; aperture generally rounded.

Habitat: Hard water, mainly in small habitats, e.g. ditches and ponds, widely distributed, England, Wales (except west), Ireland (mainly N.E. and central), S. Scotland.

Planorbis carinatus Müller

Height: 3 mm; *Breadth:* 14 mm.

Diagnostic characters: Shell thin, rather like *P. planorbis* but flatter with sharp keel near middle of periphery; 5 whorls, last relatively broader than in preceding species; glossy surface, yellowy-brown; aperture more oval.

Habitat: In hard waters, generally as for *P. planorbis* but in larger habitats, e.g. canals, rivers, and lakes; distribution as for *P. planorbis* but less often in S. Scotland.

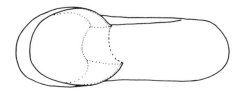

Planorbarius corneus

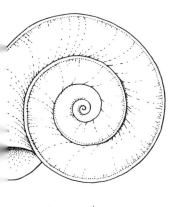

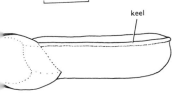

keel

Planorbis planorbis

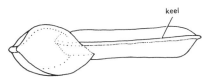

keel

Planorbis carinatus

Planorbis vortex (L.)

Height: 1.5 mm; *Breadth:* 8 mm.

Diagnostic characters: Shell forms a very thin flat disc with prominent keeled· edge; 6–7 whorls; pale yellow-brown; aperture angular and rhomboidal.

Habitat: In hard, running water with weeds; widely distributed in England and E. Wales, local in Scotland and Ireland.

Planorbis leucostoma Millet [*P. spirorbis* (L.)]

Height: 1 mm; *Breadth:* 6.5 mm.

Diagnostic characters: Shell slightly smaller than preceding species, with six more rounded whorls; brownish colour; aperture rounder than in *P. vortex* and usually supported by a white rib.

Habitat: Generally distributed (sporadic in northern Scotland), in ponds and ditches; resists drying conditions.

Planorbis crista (L.) [*P. nautileus* (L.)]

Height: 0.5 mm; *Breadth:* 2 mm.

Diagnostic characters: Shell tiny, thin-walled, 3–4 whorls, with pronounced curved transverse ridges forming points at outer margin (smooth forms do, however, occur); brown, may be darkly encrusted; in life, the mantle cavity is filled with water.

Habitat: Distributed throughout British Isles in most freshwater localities, mainly on water plants, both in stagnant and flowing waters

Planorbis albus Müller

Height: 1 mm; *Breadth:* 5 mm.

Diagnostic characters: Shell small, thin with 4–5 whorls; dull greyish-white surface, criss-crossed with spiral and transverse markings; aperture oval; in contrast to other planorbids, the blood lacks haemoglobin.

Habitat: Generally distributed in all freshwaters of the British Isles, except N.W. Scotland, usually amongst vegetation; found also on weeds in ponds and lakes but much more local in distribution is *P. laevis* Alder, distinguished from *P. albus* by a smaller, browner and smoother-surfaced shell.

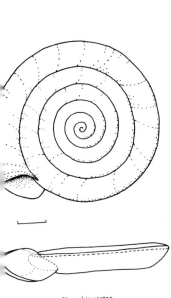

Planorbis vortex

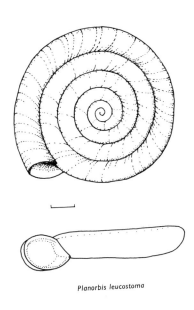

Planorbis leucostoma

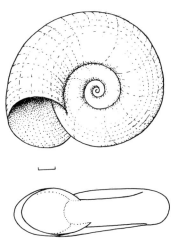

Planorbis crista

Planorbis albus

Planorbis contortus (L.)

Height: 2 mm; *Breadth:* 6 mm.

Diagnostic characters: Shell small, a thick discoid shape; 7–8 compact whorls taller than broad, forming deep-set spire; yellowish-brown; aperture crescent-shaped.

Habitat: Generally distributed, in most habitats.

Segmentina complanata (L.) [*Planorbis complanatus* (L.)]

Height: 1 mm; *Breadth:* 4 mm.

Diagnostic characters: Shell very small, thin, forming bi-convex disc; 4 rapidly increasing whorls; surface glossy, pale yellowish-brown; aperture shaped like arrow-head.

Habitat: In hard water throughout most of British Isles, except W. and N. Scotland.

Ancylus fluviatilis Müller

Height: 3 mm; *Breadth:* 5 mm; *Length:* 7 mm.

Diagnostic characters: Shell thin, limpet-like, generally oval viewed from above; apex arched and almost median, or slightly inclined to the right-hand side.

Habitat: Adheres to stones or rocks in flowing water, and also in the wave zone of lakes; widely distributed throughout British Isles, common.

General features: This species and *Acroloxus* below constitute the freshwater limpets, unrelated to their marine namesakes but like them securely attached to the substrate. They are highly adapted to aquatic life, the mantle cavity being almost lacking, and part of the mantle operates as a respiratory structure.

Acroloxus [*Ancylus*] *lacustris* (L.)

Height: 2 mm; *Breadth:* 3.5 mm; *Length:* 8 mm.

Diagnostic characters: Shell delicate, limpet-like, flatter and less broad than *Ancylus fluviatilis*, apex smaller and tending to the left.

Habitat: Favours hard water; attached to stem and underside of leaves of weeds or on timber in slow-moving or standing waters, i.e. in quieter conditions than *A. fluviatilis;* generally distributed but more restricted than the preceding species; rarer in north and west Scotland, Wales, S.W. England and less frequent in Ireland.

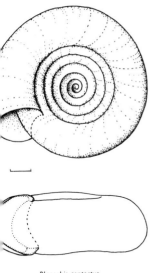

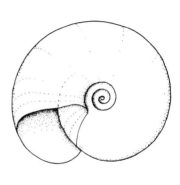

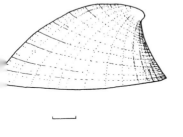

Planorbis contortus

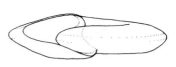

Segmentina complanata

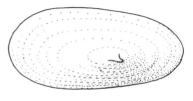

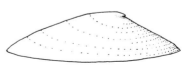

Ancylus fluviatilis

Acroloxus lacustris

Key to Terrestrial Gastropoda

Note—Bracketed sizes in this key indicate shell height.

1. Shell well developed and spiral   2
   Shell reduced (Slugs)   41
2. Snail with thick and calcareous (limy) operculum   ..   ..
                          Pomatias elegans (p. 102)
   Snail without operculum   3
3. Shell very small, 3 mm or less in height and/or breadth   ..   4
   Shell larger, more than 3 mm tall or broad   10
4. Shell (2 mm) sinistral, i.e. aperture to the left; aperture with
   6–7 teeth ..   ..   *Vertigo pusilla* (p. 106)
   Shell dextral, i.e. aperture to the right   5
5. Aperture bears teeth on inside   6
                    (see, however, *Columella*, p. 106)
   Aperture without teeth   7
6. Shell (2 mm) usually dumpy, brown; aperture typically with
   4–6 teeth ..   ..   *Vertigo* spp. (p. 106)
                    (except *V. pusilla*—4 above)
   Shell spindle-shaped, white; aperture with 3 teeth   ..   ..
                          Carychium spp. (p. 102)
7. Shell (2 mm) with prominent spines and ridges on surface ..
                      Acanthinula aculeata (p. 110)
   Shell surface smooth   8
8. Shell conical (2·5 mm), top-shaped; glossy brown   ..   ..
                          Euconulus fulvus (p. 124)
   Shell distinctly flattened   9
9. Minute, brown shell (1·5 mm across)   *Punctum pygmaeum* (p. 124)
   Shell whitish, 2·5 mm broad; lip of aperture reflected   ..
                          Vallonia spp. (p. 108)
   Shell rather transparent, whitish or with faint greenish tinge,
   3 mm broad; lip of aperture not reflected   *Vitrea* spp. (p. 124)

10. Shell sinistral 11
    Shell dextral 13

11. Shell (7 mm) aperture usually without teeth; on walls and
    tree trunks .. .. *Balea perversa* (p. 112)
    Shell taller (10 mm or more), club-shaped; aperture with teeth
    and folds, and occupied also by a 'sliding door' or clausilium 12

12. Prominent plaits or folds within outer lip; shell surface smooth
    Marpessa laminata (p. 110)
    Folds inside lip of aperture less prominent; shell surface com-
    monly ridged or striated .. .. *Clausilia* spp. (p. 112)

13. Aperture usually bears teeth on inside 14
    Aperture without teeth 17

14. Aperture with one tooth 15
    Aperture with more than one tooth 16

15. Shell (4 mm) bluntly tapering, oval aperture .. ..
    Lauria cylindracea (p. 108)
    Shell (3·5 mm) dumpy; round aperture *Pupilla muscorum* (p. 108)

16. Shell (6·5 mm) shiny brown, spindly, shallow suture; aperture
    usually with 3 teeth .. .. .. *Azeca goodalli* (p. 104)
    Shell (8 mm) with striated surface; cylindrical towards base,
    medium suture; aperture with 8–9 teeth *Abida secale* (p. 108)
    (see also *Phytia, Leucophytia*, p. 74)

17. Shell tall-spired 18
    Shell less tall or with reduced spire, often cone-shaped or
    flatter 19

18. Shell (6·5 mm) very glossy, pale brown *Cochlicopa* spp. (p. 104)
    Shell taller (9–15 mm) brownish, white reflected lip to aper-
    ture .. .. *Ena* spp. (p. 110)
    Shell (19 mm) with very elongated conical spire; pale, opaque,
    with brownish markings and, typically a dark band towards
    base; found near coastal areas *Cochlicella acuta* (p. 122)
    (see also *Ceciloides*, p. 112)

19. Shell surface hairy or bristly 20
    Shell surface smooth 21

20. Shell (4·5 mm) surface covered with prominent whitish hairs lying in oblique rows; narrow umbilicus; aperture without strong rib   ..   ..   ..   *Monacha granulata* (p. 120)
Shell (5 mm) surface covered with short hairs; wide umbilicus; prominent white rib inside aperture   *Hygromia hispida* (p. 118)
(see also young *H. striolata* below—34)

21. Shell usually with complete or incomplete coloured bands ..   22
Shell not banded   29
(for exceptions see below—*Cepaea* spp.)

22. Shell large (30 mm or more)   23
Shell smaller (less than 30 mm)   24

23. Very large (45 mm), thick-walled shell; generally pale-coloured but with brownish bands; locally on calcareous soils ..   ..
Helix pomatia Roman, edible or apple snail (p. 114)
Shell somewhat smaller (30 mm); light brown with darker, irregular bands; common, abundant in gardens   ..   ..
Helix aspersa Common garden snail (p. 114)

24. Shell surface dull, wrinkled or ridged; (6·5 mm tall, 10 mm broad)   ..   ..   *Helicella caperata* (p. 120)
Shell surface smoother and glossier   25

25. Shell very disc-shaped, (20 mm broad)   *Helicella itala* (p. 122)
Shell generally cone-shaped   26

26. Aperture with prominent white, reflexed lip   27
Lip of aperture variably coloured, but often darker; not typically white and reflexed   28

27. Shell (18 mm) brown or purple-brown, but characteristically flecked with yellow or other lighter colours, usually with darker peripheral band ..   ..   ..   *Arianta arbustorum* (p. 116)
Shell (14 mm) usually yellow background, but may be pink, brown or otherwise coloured, with, typically, 5 dark bands; there is however much variation, including fusion of bands, and unbanded forms ..   ..   ..   *Cepaea hortensis* (p. 116)

28. Shell (17 mm), showing same range of colour and band variations as *Cepaea hortensis* (see above); aperture with deep brown lip; umbilicus closed in adult ..   *Cepaea nemoralis* (p. 116)
Shell smaller (11 mm), white with brown bands and a brown apex; narrow but prominent deep umbilicus ..   ..   ..
Helicella virgata (p. 122)

29. Shell taller than broad; thin-walled and amber-coloured; very
    large body whorl making up 4/5 of height; aperture large,
    pointed above; on or near waterside plants *Succinea* spp. (p. 104)
    Shell broader than tall 30
30. Shell cone-shaped (14 mm); surface pale, hairy in young but
    smooth in adult; reddish colour towards aperture, which is
    strengthened internally by a white rib ..   ..
    Monacha cantiana (p. 120)
    Shell flattened and disc-shaped   31
31. Shell with strong transverse ridges; lens-(discus-) shaped with
    radiating reddish-brown streaks; 6·5 mm broad   ..   ..
    Discus rotundatus (p. 124)
    Shell smoother and/or otherwise shaped or coloured   .. 32
32. Aperture large, half the width of the shell, which is fragile,
    translucent and greenish; 5 mm broad *Vitrina pellucida* (p. 130)
    Aperture less than half the shell width 33
33. Body whorl keeled   34
    No keel 35
34. Body whorl sharply keeled; prominent white, reflexed lip;
    17 mm broad   ..   ..   ..   *Helicigona lapicida* (p. 118)
    Body whorl bluntly keeled; younger shells have more pro-
    minent keel and bear bristles; brownish shell, often with paler
    peripheral band; 13 mm broad   *Hygromia striolata* (p. 118)
    (see also *H. hispida* above—20)
35. Shell approximately 4 mm broad*   36
    Shell typically larger   37
36. Brownish shell with distinct radiating striations; narrow
    umbilicus   ..   ..   ..   *Retinella radiatula* (p. 128)
    Shell paler, less prominently striated   *Retinella pura* (p. 128)
37. Shell surface very shiny and glossy giving polished appear-
    ance (*Oxychilus*) 38
    Shell surface less shiny; often more waxy or silky in texture .. 40
38. Up to 14 mm broad   ..   *Oxychilus draparnaldi* (p. 128)
    Shell smaller   ..   .. ,   .. 39

*The following disc-shaped snails, especially species of *Oxychilus* and *Retinella*,
are difficult to separate. Beginners are advised to consult the admirable key by
Morton and Machin (for details see Appendix) in which useful diagnostic
features of living members of these genera as well as shell characters are included.

39. 10 mm broad, very flattened and discoid, aperture elliptical; $5\frac{1}{2}$
    whorls; animal pale grey   ..   *Oxychilus cellarius* (p. 126)
    8 mm broad, slightly elevated spire, roundish aperture and
    small umbilicus; 5 whorls; jet-black edge to mantle shows
    through margin of shell   ..   *Oxychilus helveticus* (p. 126)
    Smaller, 5 mm broad; $4-4\frac{1}{2}$ whorls; animal dark but mantle
    not black-edged; smells of garlic when irritated   ..   ..
    　　　　　　　　　　　　　　　　Oxychilus alliarius (p. 126)

40. Reddish-brown shell, 7 mm broad, with whorls only slowly
    increasing; roundish aperture and slightly elevated spire;
    animal with dark spot on mantle edge; very wet localities ..
    　　　　　　　　　　　　　　　　Zonitoides nitidus (p. 128)
    Similarly sized shell with dull horny or waxy surface; last
    whorl slightly flared; flattened spire, elliptical aperture;
    mantle without spot; in drier habitats .. *Retinella nitidula* (p. 128)

41. Small external shell borne by mantle at posterior end of body
    　　　　　　　　　　　　　　　　Testacella spp. (p. 130)
    Mantle visible and shield-like at anterior end of body enclos-
    ing rudimentary internal shell and bearing respiratory opening
    on its right hand side   42

42. Respiratory opening towards
    anterior end of mantle; body
    without keel (*Arion*)   ..   43

    Respiratory opening pos-
    terior to the centre of the
    mantle; body keeled   ..   46

43. Very large slug, 140 mm long when fully extended;
    (a) usually dark-coloured: *Arion ater ater*   ..   (p. 132)
    (b) usually reddish or yellowish: *Arion ater rufus*   ..   (p. 132)
    Much smaller   44

44. 60 mm long; yellow to brown with yellowish-white foot
    　　　　　　　　　　　　　　　　Arion subfuscus (p. 134)
    35 mm or less in length   45

45. Small, stocky, with prominent tubercles; surface appears
prickly when contracted; 20 mm long ..*Arion intermedius* (p. 132)
Slightly larger (30 mm long); dark back; prominent dark
lateral bands on body and mantle, that on right side enclosing
respiratory opening; appears semi-circular in end view when
contracted; yellow to orange foot; common

Arion hortensis (p. 134)
35 mm long; also with dark lateral bands but that on right side
arches over respiratory opening; animal has bell-shaped
appearance in end-view when contracted; opaque white foot;
common .. .. .. *Arion circumscriptus* (p. 134)

46. Mantle with rough and granular surface, and divided by a
furrow; prominent keel extending length of body from tail to
rear end of mantle .. .. .. *Milax* spp. (p. 136)
Mantle surface bears delicate concentric ridges; no furrow;
body keeled only at posterior end 47

47. Back slopes gently towards tail which is pointed; centre point
of the concentric mantle ridges occurs in mid-dorsal line;
posterior end of mantle pointed; mantle and body often
banded (*Limax*) 48
Back slopes steeply downwards at tip of tail; centre point of
the concentric mantle ridges lies to right of mid-line; posterior
end of mantle rounded; mantle and body not banded (*Agriolimax*) 49

48. Large slug, 150 mm long when extended; mantle shield with
darker spots; two to three broken dark longitudinal bands on
either side of body; tentacles brown *Limax maximus* (p. 136)
About 85 mm long; mantle shield and body with yellow spots;
tentacles steel-blue .. .. .. *Limax flavus* (p. 136)
Body very translucent and gelatinous due to high water content; 75 mm long .. *Lehmannia marginata* (p. 138)

49. Variably-coloured slug, but usually yellowish-brown with
darker markings giving a reticulated appearance; 35 mm long
when extended; sticky white mucus; very common .. ..
Agriolimax reticulatus (p. 138)
Smaller, barely 25 mm long when extended; brown with paler
mantle; colourless mucus; usually in marshy conditions ..
Agriolimax laevis (p. 138)

Pomatias elegans (Müller)

Height: 15 mm; *Breadth:* 10 mm.

Diagnostic characters: Shell largely conical, $4\frac{1}{2}$–5 whorls, larger ones with spiral ridges traversed by cross-striations; aperture nearly circular, closed by thick, calcified operculum; greyish- to pinkish-brown but variably coloured; one pair of tentacles with eyes at base.

Habitat: On chalky soils and in limestone districts requiring calcium carbonate content of at least 5%, i.e. calcicole species; often in hedges or scrub, associated with damp leafy soil, moss or other vegetation; England and Wales, mainly in the south and east (northern colonies showing decline).

General features: This is one of the few terrestrial representatives of the primitive (prosobranch) snails which are so characteristic of the marine environment. The gill has been lost and respiration is carried out by the vascular wall of the mantle cavity. Another operculate land snail, but with a horny, not limy, operculum, is the tiny (2·5 mm) *Acicula [Acme] fusca* (Montagu). This bears a shiny, cylindrical shell, and is found living in damp localities amongst leaves and moss in wild places, e.g. old woodlands, habitats popular with terrestrial molluscs.

Carychium tridentatum (Risso)

Height: 2 mm; *Breadth:* 1 mm.

Diagnostic characters: Shell minute, 5 whorls with stubby apex; aperture with 3 tooth-like processes, evenly sited within the lips of the aperture; white; no operculum.

Habitat: In damp localities amongst leaf-mould, moss, under logs etc.; widely distributed.

General features: This introduces the true pulmonates, non-operculate with a pulmonary cavity, which constitute the bulk of the land Mollusca. *Carychium* is a primitive form with two pairs of tentacles, the anterior rudimentary, with eyes at the base of the posterior pair (basommatophoran condition). The remainder bear eyes at the tip of the rear tentacles (stylommatophoran). The similar, but relatively shorter and broader, *C. minimum* Müller, with $4\frac{1}{2}$ whorls to the shell, sometimes distinguished also by a less prominent tooth on the outer lip, is also widely distributed but inhabits much wetter localities, e.g. marshes.

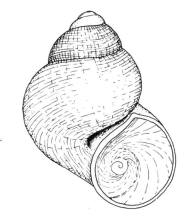

Pomatias elegans

Acicula fusca

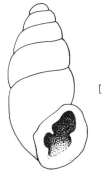

Carychium tridentatum

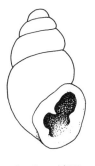

Carychium minimum

Succinea putris (L.)

Height: 16 mm; *Breadth:* 10 mm.

Diagnostic characters: Shell thin-walled, oval, spire reduced; 4 whorls, the body whorl relatively very large and swollen; pale amber; large aperture, into which the animal cannot fully withdraw; no umbilicus.

Habitat: In damp, marshy locations, including wet meadows, on vegetation; England, Wales and Ireland, but few verified records in Scotland.

General features: The soft-bodied *Succinea* is a hygrophile, i.e. it requires wet, marshy conditions in which to live. Like other damp-loving snails, *S. putris* harbours the intermediate stages of parasitic flukes, in this case, *Leuchloridium macrostomum*, the brightly coloured larval cysts of which come to lie in the tentacles. Another species, *S. pfeifferi* Rossmässler is smaller (10 mm), slightly narrower and darker, widespread but commoner in the North, and tends to inhabit even wetter locations than *S. putris*, being nearly amphibious in habit. Also in very wet localities, sometimes on floating leaves, is the slenderer still *S. elegans* Risso, but this species is limited to the Norfolk Broads, and to a few similar fenlands in the S.E.

Azeca goodalli (Férussac)

Height: 6·5 mm; *Breadth:* 2·5 mm.

Diagnostic characters: Shell broadly spindle-shaped; 7 whorls with shallow suture; blunted apex; surface shiny brown; aperture with three, sometimes more, teeth.

Habitat: In damp leaf mould and moss, locally distributed in woods and hedges in England and Wales.

Cochlicopa lubrica (Müller)

Height: 6·5 mm; *Breadth:* 2·5 mm.

Diagnostic characters: Shell elongate and rather oval; 6 whorls with moderately well marked suture and stubby apex; very glossy surface, pale brown and translucent; aperture without teeth.

Habitat: Widespread throughout British Isles in damp locations in moss, rotting leaves and turf; somewhat more local than *C. lubrica*, and in drier localities, one finds the slimmer and smaller (5 mm) *C. lubricella* (Porro) [*C. minima* (Siemaschko)]

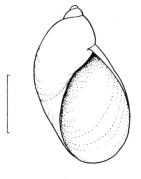

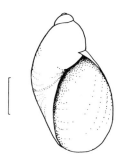

Succinea putris

Succinea pfeifferi

Azeca goodalli

Cochlicopa lubrica

Vertigo pygmaea (Draparnaud)

Height: 2 mm; *Breadth:* 1 mm.

Diagnostic characters: Shell tiny, plump and oval; 5 whorls, dextrally coiled, the body whorl bearing a rounded rib behind the outer lip; glossy, brown; aperture usually with 4–5 teeth.

Habitat: Generally distributed, both in wild, e.g. marshes, meadows, woods, and in cultivated areas, under stones, logs, etc.

General features: This is the commonest of the species of *Vertigo*, all characterised by minute, rather dumpy, shells, which, with those of the closely-related *Abida* and *Lauria* (see below), bear an aperture typically provided with well developed teeth, up to 9 in some species. These are probably an effective protection, in lieu of an operculum, against potential predators, especially insects. In wetter places, one might come across the species *V. antivertigo* (Draparnaud), typically with 6 teeth around the aperture, and, particularly in the broads, the larger *V. moulinsiana* (Dupuy). Mention might be made here also of the similarly sized but toothless *Columella edentula* (Draparnaud), quite widespread in woodlands and damp localities, including marshes.

Vertigo pusilla Müller

Height: 2 mm; *Breadth:* 1 mm.

Diagnostic characters: Shell tiny, generally similar in form to *V. pygmaea* above, but sinistral; slightly paler colour; aperture usually with 6 teeth.

Habitat: Locally distributed on dry walls and banks, amongst dead leaves, ivy and moss; more often found in northern counties, also Scotland and in certain parts of Ireland.

General features: This snail represents one of two rather rare sinistral species of *Vertigo*, most other members of which, as described above, are typically dextral. Also worth including here is the not unrelated *Pyramidula rupestris* (Draparnaud), a tiny (2 mm) top-shaped species, which like *V. pusilla* is a 'wall' snail; it is in fact always found living on old stone walls and rocks in limestone areas, especially in western counties with a high annual rainfall.

[

Vertigo pygmaea

[

Vertigo pusilla

[

Vertigo antivertigo

[

Columella edentula

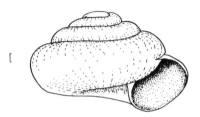

[

Pyramidula rupestris

Pupilla muscorum (L.)

Height: 3·5 mm; *Breadth:* 1·75 mm.

Diagnostic characters: Shell small, rather dumpy and cylindrical, thick-walled; brownish; aperture round, typically with single tooth on the inner parietal wall.

Habitat: In turf, under stones, on walls, rocks and dry places generally, including sandhills, avoiding woodlands; generally distributed, but rather local and uncommon in Scotland.

Lauria cylindracea (da Costa)

Height: 4 mm; *Breadth:* 2 mm.

Diagnostic characters: Shell small, thin, rather cylindrical, but with a bluntly tapering spire; glossy, pale yellow-brown; aperture oval with white flange-like lip and usually with one tooth on inner parietal side.

Habitat: Widely distributed, under leaves or turf, in woods, grass, hedges and on walls and cliffs.

Abida secale (Draparnaud)

Height: 7 mm; *Breadth:* 3 mm.

Diagnostic characters: Shell appears like a chrysalis, long and bluntly pointed; surface striated, brownish; outer lip swollen; aperture bears 8–9 prominent teeth or folds.

Habitat: Locally distributed in limestone areas, on grassy hillsides, rocks and in open woods; England, but not eastern counties (a relict species, like several calciphiles showing some tendency to decline).

Vallonia costata (Müller)

Height: 1·2 mm; *Breadth:* 2·5 mm.

Diagnostic characters: Shell tiny, disc-shaped; 3–4 whorls, the body whorl large; ribbed surface, greyish-yellow; aperture round with reflected lip and white internal rib; broad umbilicus.

Habitat: In dry localities, e.g. in grass and amongst dried leaves, generally avoiding woodland; widely distributed, but less universal in Scotland. In similar habitats one also finds the smooth shelled, slightly smaller *V. excentrica* Sterki, but the third British species *V. pulchella* (Müller), whitish, and also with a relatively smooth surface, is rarer, found mostly in rather wet places, e.g. in damp lowland areas.

Lauria cylindracea

Pupilla muscorum

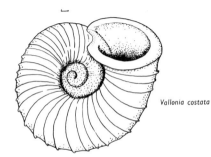

Vallonia costata

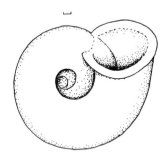

Vallonia excentrica

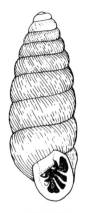

Abida secale

Acanthinula aculeata (Müller)

Height: 2 mm; *Breadth:* 2 mm.

Diagnostic characters: Shell minute, rather top-shaped, with 4 whorls bearing prominent ribs drawn out into spiny processes of the periostracum, giving prickly appearance; brown; open umbilicus.

Habitat: Generally distributed, mainly in woodlands and hedges, amongst fallen leaves.

Ena obscura (Müller)

Height: 9 mm; *Breadth:* 4 mm.

Diagnostic characters: Shell generally oval with rather long, bluntly-tapering apex; 7 whorls; surface faintly ridged, pale brown; outer lip of aperture white and reflected; narrow umbilicus.

Habitat: Found especially in woods and hedges in limestone areas; generally distributed in British Isles, except for appreciable areas in Scotland and Ireland (the larger, darker brown *Ena montana* (Draparnaud) (15 mm high) is a rare species restricted to warmer southern counties of England amongst fallen leaves in old woodlands, on limestone.)

Marpessa laminata (Montagu)

Height: 16 mm; *Breadth:* 4 mm.

Diagnostic characters: Shell sinistral, long and club-shaped, up to 12 whorls, the first three or four increasing only slowly; surface glossy, yellow-brown; aperture with 2 strong folds and 3 or 4 deeper ridges inside a strong, white reflected lip, which bears one prominent tooth; clausilium present (see below).

Habitat: Typically found in crevices on tree-trunks, logs and fallen branches associated with moss and lichens on which it feeds, sometimes in woods and hedges; generally distributed in England, only occasionally elsewhere in British Isles.

General features: This species and *Clausilia* below have characteristically elongated, club-shaped sinistral shells, with folds and teeth protecting the aperture. As in *Vertigo* (see above, p. 106), these are of protective value and this function is enhanced by the presence of the clausilium, a flexible, sliding plate which acts as a door over the aperture when the snail withdraws. Only one member of this family, *Balea* (see page 112), typically lacks these features.

Acanthinula aculeata

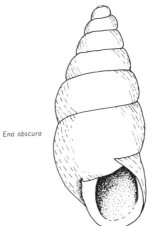

Ena obscura

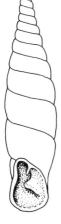

Marpessa laminata

Clausilia bidentata (Ström)

Height: 10 mm; *Breadth:* 2·5 mm.

Diagnostic characters: Shell also sinistral and club-shaped; 12–13 whorls, the first three parallel sided; surface finely striated especially across the whorls (appear vertical almost in shell); pale brown with white streaks; aperture rather small and drawn out into a sinus at upper corner; lip bears 2 teeth and also folds occur within the lip; clausilium.

Habitat: Throughout British Isles, in woods, hedges, and on tree-trunks and walls, both wild and cultivated areas.

General features: Several *Clausilia* species and related snails feed largely at night on lichens and moss, found by climbing up surfaces after spending the day partly hidden in cracks or between tree roots. However, the broader and lighter coloured (12 mm) *C. rolphii* Turton is purely a ground species and never climbs; it is found locally in central and southern England in hedges and woodland. The rarer, larger (16 mm) *C. dubia* Draparnaud is restricted to the north.

Balea perversa (L.)

Height: 7 mm; *Breadth:* 2·5 mm.

Diagnostic characters: Shell sinistral, club-shaped, but with a less parallel sided apex than in *Clausilia* and *Marpessa*; 6–8 whorls; surface glossy, striated, brownish colour; aperture usually without teeth or folds, although parietal region may bear one small process; no clausilium (contrast other members of Clausiliidae described above).

Habitat: Mainly in crevices on tree-trunks especially those of elm, apple and willow with rough bark, and also on walls, feeding on moss or lichens, rarely on the ground; generally, although rather locally, distributed.

General features: This snail has a well defined tree-living habit, thereby tending to avoid competition with other molluscs. Not unrelated to *Balea* and with an equally unusual way of life, is *Ceciloides acicula* (Müller), a blind snail with a small (5 mm), dextral, transparent and needle-shaped shell (appearing white when dead or bleached) which lives buried in soil and turf and under boulders in limestone areas. It is sometimes known as the grave-digger's snail because of its predilection for churchyards.

Clausilia bidentata

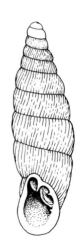

Clausilia rolphi

Clausilia dubia

Balea perversa

Ceciloides acicula

Helix aspersa Müller   Common garden snail

Height: 30 mm; *Breadth:* 34 mm.

Diagnostic characters: Shell large, solid and globular, $4\frac{1}{2}$–5 whorls, the body whorl being very swollen and making up a large proportion of the shell; medium sized, bluntly rounded spire; background colour fawn with variegated darker brown markings, often forming up to 5 broken bands; large roundish aperture with white thickened lip; umbilicus closed.

Habitat: Very common in gardens and cultivated areas (anthropophile or synanthropic species, i.e. associated with man); favours stone walls and churchyards, also widespread in scrubland, rough herbage, woods, hedges, quarries and amongst rocks in limestone areas; tends to occur in groups (gregarious); widely distributed, except northern Scotland, although northward spread facilitated by man.

General features: The garden snail introduces the large and successful pulmonate family, Helicidae, the so-called 'typical snails'. These largely herbivorous gastropods show a wide range of adaptations to most terrestrial habitats and the ensuing variability of form and structure creates difficulties in identifying species on the basis of shell characters alone. *Helix*, in common with other helicids, resists desiccation by using an epiphragm (p. 19) to seal the aperture when inactive in summer (aestivation) or winter months (hibernation).

Helix pomatia L.   Roman, edible or apple snail

Height: 45 mm; *Breadth:* 45 mm.

Diagnostic characters: Shell very large, thick-walled; shaped generally as for *H. aspersa* but surface less smooth, with coarse striations; cream or pale brown in colour, with up to five rather faint spiral bands; aperture rounded but relatively taller than in *H. aspersa;* umbilicus a narrow crack; epiphragm hard and chalky.

Habitat: Requires limestone and calcareous soils (calcicole species) in open woodlands and on downs; not cultivated areas; less gregarious than *H. aspersa*; southern England, locally distributed.

General features: This, the largest British land snail, has, like other helicids, a complex reproductive system and courtship behaviour pattern which ensures cross-fertilisation. During mating a calcareous 'love-dart,' the shape of which can be diagnostic (see p. 116), is ejected from each partner into the body of the other as a means of stimulation.

Helix aspersa

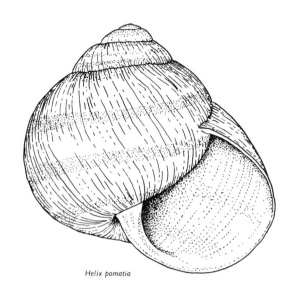

Helix pomatia

Arianta arbustorum (L.)

Height: 18 mm; *Breadth:* 22 mm.

Diagnostic characters: Shell thick-walled, globular, 5–6 rounded whorls; surface glossy, brown with lighter flecks and usually darker peripheral band although albinos may occur; lip of aperture white and reflexed.

Habitat: Widespread in wilder localities, including moist woodlands, marshes and river banks associated with dense vegetation, although occasionally on blown sand and in drier localities, e.g. the dunes of northern Scotland; generally distributed in Great Britain, but local in all except southern Ireland.

Cepaea nemoralis (L.)

Height: 17 mm; *Breadth:* 22 mm.

Diagnostic characters: Shell globular, quite thickly built, with a blunt rounded spire; $5\frac{1}{2}$ whorls; background colour typically yellowish with 5 darker spiral bands, but colour very variable, e.g. also brown or pink in general colour, as is the number of bands, some or all of which may be missing; aperture usually with dark brown lip.

Habitat: Generally distributed in woods, hedges, on downs, etc., throughout British Isles except northern parts of Scotland.

General features: The land snail, *Cepaea*, is noted for its variable shell colour patterns which are genetically determined (polymorphism). The pattern varies according to habitat thereby enabling the snail to hide from its major predator, the thrush. Yellow banded shells, for example, which appear greenish with the animal inside, are relatively more abundant in hedgerows and rough herbage where they are less conspicuous, whereas in beech woods, carpeted in brownish leaves, the better camouflaged unbanded brown or pink-shelled forms occur in greater proportion.

Cepaea hortensis (Müller)

Height: 14 mm; *Breadth:* 18 mm.

Diagnostic characters: Shell similar in shape to *C. nemoralis* but somewhat smaller and thinner-walled; outer lip of aperture typically white and reflexed; 5 whorls, rather more rounded than in above species; typically yellow with up to 5 dark spiral bands, but same variability of pattern as in *C. nemoralis* (the only sure guide for separating these two species is the shape of the dart, straight in *C. nemoralis*, curved in *C. hortensis*, and its appearance in cross-section—see figure opposite).

Habitat: As for *C. nemoralis* but local in Ireland.

Arianta arbustorum

Cepaea nemoralis

Cepaea hortensis

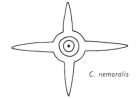

C. nemoralis

Darts (T.S.)

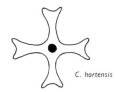

C. hortensis

Hygromia striolata (C. Pfeiffer)

Height: 8 mm; *Breadth:* 13 mm.

Diagnostic characters: Shell fairly robust, depressed with a shallow spire; 6 whorls, body whorl with slight keel above periphery, better marked in young stages; greyish-white to brown, often with paler band at the edge; surface hairy in juvenile; large umbilicus; animal pale grey.

Habitat: In gardens, where it is a pest on strawberries, and also in damp localities on waysides (mainly on broad leaved plants), woods and hedges, amongst leaves and litter; generally distributed, except northern Scotland; its spread to northern and western areas has probably been facilitated by man's influence.

Hygromia hispida (L.)

Height: 5 mm; *Breadth:* 9 mm.

Diagnostic characters: Shell also depressed but smaller; 6–7 whorls; greyish-brown surface covered with short curved hairs arising from the periostracum, more pronounced than in a young *H. stroilata*; no keel (contrast *H. striolata*); white rib just within outer lip of aperture; usually wide umbilicus; animal darker grey.

Habitat: Generally distributed, up to north Scotland, in moist localities, e.g. under logs, less frequent in cultivated areas.

General features: Much more restricted to wild areas is *H. subrufescens* (Miller), with a thin and membranous (9 mm broad) amber-coloured, coarsely wrinkled shell. It is an anthropophobe species, i.e. avoiding localities inhabited and influenced by man. Also limited, in this case to the south-west, near the sea, is *H. subvirescens* (Bellamy), with a small (6 mm broad) well camouflaged, green and hairy shell. Another hairy-shelled snail is the very rare *Helicodonta obvoluta* (Müller), with a characteristic discoid shell; this species is limited to old woodlands on the South Downs.

Helicigona lapicida (L.)

Height: 7 mm; *Breadth:* 17 mm.

Diagnostic characters: Shell well-built, flattened, with a clearly-keeled body whorl; brownish with darker red-brown markings; aperture with a broad, reflected white lip.

Habitat: Locally distributed in limestone areas; England, Devon, north to Yorkshire, but not N.W.; eastern Wales; Ireland only in Cork; found in beech woods, and on walls and rocks in crevices.

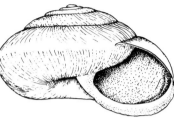

Hygromia striolata

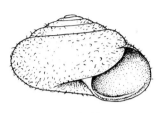

Hygromia hispida

Helicodonta obvoluta

Helicigona lapicida

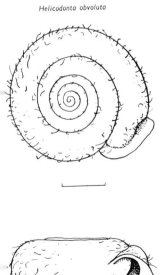

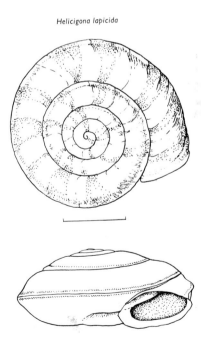

Monacha granulata (Alder)

Height: 5 mm; *Breadth:* 7·5 mm.

Diagnostic characters: Shell small, thin-walled, rather globular, consisting of 6 whorls; surface greyish-yellow, covered with prominent, whitish hairs arising from the periostracum, lying in oblique rows; very narrow umbilicus.

Habitat: In damp, shaded areas, amongst vegetation, but in dry places in west, e.g. hedgerows in Devon and Cornwall; generally distributed in England and Wales, local in Scotland and rare in Ireland.

Monacha cantiana (Montagu)

Height: 14 mm; *Breadth:* 20 mm.

Diagnostic characters: Shell globular, 6–6½ whorls; glossy surface, slightly hairy in young stages, whitish with red tinge on lower surface and near aperture; aperture roundish with brown lip; deep but small umbilicus.

Habitat: In grassy areas and on banks amongst nettles, in hedgerows and waste ground; an expanding species despite its popular name ('Kentish snail'), generally distributed in England, except N.W. and Cornwall, also Glamorgan.

Helicella caperata (Montagu)

Height: 6·5 mm; *Breadth:* 10 mm.

Diagnostic characters: Shell solid, rather depressed but with somewhat elevated, blunt spire with brown apex; 4½–5 whorls; surface dull, prominently striated transversely, giving wrinkled appearance; background colour pale, white or cream, usually with variable, often broken, spiral dark brown or purplish bands, which tend to be thinner and more complete on lower surface; lip of aperture strengthened by white internal rib.

Habitat: On calcareous, usually dry grassy soils, on downs, banks or sand-dunes, also on way-sides on narrow-leaved plants; widely distributed.

General features: Helicella and related species, the 'Sandhill snails', are xerophiles, resistant to desiccation in the dry and often exposed habitats in which they live. Their shells are typically strongly built and protectively pigmented. Living in similar habitats to other *Helicella* species, but not so widespread and frequent, is *H. gigaxi* (L. Pfeiffer); this resembles *H. caperata* but the shell bears finer and more regular striations and the umbilicus is less centrally placed.

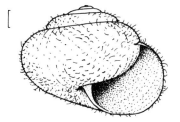

Monacha granulata

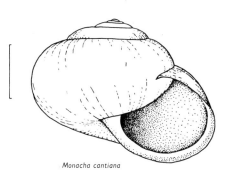

Monacha cantiana

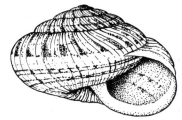

Helicella caperata

Helicella virgata (da Costa)

Height: 11 mm; *Breadth:* 15 mm.

Diagnostic characters: Shell larger and more globular than *H. caperata* although variable, with more raised conical apex; 5–6 whorls; rather thin-walled; smooth surface, finely-striated; white or cream, with thick dark brown band towards upper surface, and several thinner bands on lower side.

Habitat: As for *H. caperata*, on dry, grassy localities, including sand-dunes, on calcareous ground; frequent and widely distributed in England and Wales, more local and sparse in Scotland, Ireland, except northern parts.

Helicella itala (L.)

Height: 9 mm; *Breadth:* 19 mm.

Diagnostic characters: Shell strong, larger and more discoid than the other species of *Helicella;* typically pale with prominent bands, a thicker one above the mid-line, although there is some variability, including blotchy forms; very broad umbilicus.

Habitat: Similar to other *Helicella* species; frequent but local in England, Ireland and Wales and parts of Scotland.

Cochlicella acuta (Müller)

Height: 19 mm; *Breadth:* 6 mm.

Diagnostic characters: Shell elongate, of 9 whorls, with long pointed conical shape; opaque, off-white or fawn with brown streaks and typically dark brown band on lower side of body whorl (darker forms do occur).

Habitat: In dry calcareous areas, usually near the sea, on grassy sand hills; found along S.W. and N. coasts of Great Britain, where it is exclusively coastal, and in Ireland, where it extends inland.

General features: This species, like the helicellids described above, is typically associated with a maritime environment. In the same category but much rarer and restricted mainly to the south-west is *Theba pisana* (Müller), characterised by a large (18 mm broad), depressed shell, opaque white and banded, but pinkish inside the lip of the aperture. *Theba* is a representative of the so-called Mediterranean-Lusitanian fauna and has probably been introduced as a casual extension of its normal centre of distribution in warmer countries south of the British Isles.

Helicella virgata

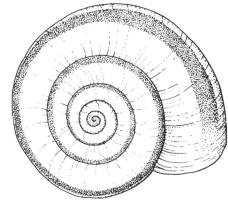

Helicella itala

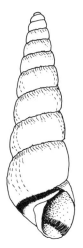

Cochlicella acuta

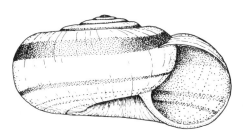

Theba pisana

Punctum pygmaeum (Draparnaud)

Height: 0·8 mm; *Breadth:* 1·5 mm.

Diagnostic characters: Shell minute, disc-shaped, thin-walled; $3\frac{1}{2}$–4 whorls; brown; aperture round; large umbilicus.

Habitat: Common on dead leaves, logs, stones and moss, favouring damp sites, in woods, hedges and marshes; widely distributed.

General features: This miniature snail along with *Discus* below comprise the primitive family Endodontidae. They are probably ancestral to the terrestrial slugs of the *Arion* type (see p. 132).

Discus rotundatus (Müller)

Height: 2·5 mm; *Breadth:* 6·5 mm.

Diagnostic characters: Shell small, disc-shaped; 6–7 whorls, increasing only gradually; surface with marked transverse ridges, yellowish-brown with darker reddish-brown radiating markings; broad umbilicus.

Habitat: Widely distributed; frequent amongst leaves, moss and débris, and under logs and rotten wood.

Euconulus fulvus (Müller)

Height: 2·3 mm; *Breadth:* 3 mm.

Diagnostic characters: Shell very small, rather top-shaped with a well marked regular spire; 5–6 whorls; reddish-brown; umbilicus hardly visible.

Habitat: Widely distributed in woods, grassy locations, under stones and in moss; also in marshes.

General features: This species introduces the Zonitidae, a family of snails, many with shiny, flattened, shells, and several of which are very common in the British terrestrial molluscan fauna.

Vitrea crystallina (Müller)

Height: 1·3 mm; *Breadth:* 2·5 mm.

Diagnostic characters: Shell very small and delicate, translucent, disc-shaped; almost 5 tightly coiled whorls; glossy, white or greenish; very narrow umbilicus.

Habitat: Generally distributed in damp areas in grass, marshes, or in woods and hedges under leaves, etc.; also widespread is *V. contracta* (Westerlund), which resembles the type species but has a milkier, more tightly coiled, shell.

Punctum pygmaeum

Discus rotundatus

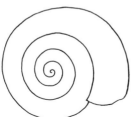

Vitrea crystallina

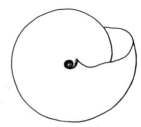

Euconulus fulvus

Oxychilus cellarius (Müller)

Height: 5 mm; *Breadth:* 10 mm.

Diagnostic characters: Shell disc-shaped, and polished, spire very depressed; $5\frac{1}{2}$ whorls; surface glossy, pale yellowish-grey or yellowish-brown, white on underside; aperture elliptical; animal grey.

Habitat: Widely distributed in damp, shaded localities in woods, especially where rich in humus, gardens, cellars and derelict buildings.

General features: Oxychilus species are ubiquitous and characterised by carnivorous tendencies, although not to the exclusion of plant and fungal material. Many give off distinctive odours. These and the species of *Retinella* and *Zonitoides* described below are difficult to distinguish on shell characters alone. Attention should be paid to the nature of the animal as an aid to identification.

Oxychilus helveticus (Blum)

Height: 5 mm; *Breadth:* 8 mm.

Diagnostic characters: Shell similar to that of *O. cellarius*, but with rounder aperture; rather more raised spire, smaller umbilicus and richer brown colour; diagnostic feature is jet-black edge to mantle visible through shell when animal is retracted.

Habitat: Local in hedgerows, waysides and woods in much of Great Britain and rare in Scotland; not present in Ireland.

Oxychilus alliarius (Miller)

Height: 2 mm; *Breadth:* 5 mm

Diagnostic characters: Shell is also discoidal, but smaller and not as flattened as *O. cellarius*; $4–4\frac{1}{2}$ whorls, spire slightly raised; glossy surface, brownish above, paler on underside; aperture broadly elliptical; animal bluish-black, smells strongly of garlic.

Habitat: Almost ubiquitous throughout British Isles.

Oxychilus draparnaldi (Beck)

Height: 6 mm; *Breadth:* 14 mm.

Diagnostic characters: Shell the largest of the *Oxychilus* species; thicker-walled, brownish; 6 whorls; body whorl somewhat expanded at the aperture; animal cobalt blue.

Habitat: Usually synanthropic, occurring in gardens and in rubbish, but found in wild and waste places in the west; carnivorous.

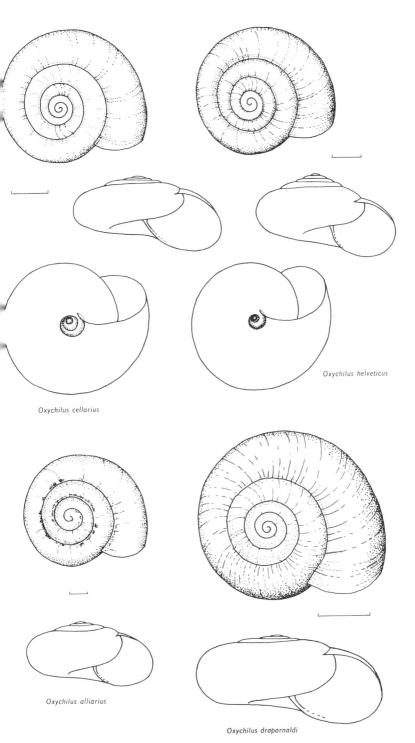

Oxychilus cellarius

Oxychilus helveticus

Oxychilus alliarius

Oxychilus draparnaldi

Retinella radiatula (Alder)

Height: 2 mm; *Breadth:* 4 mm.

Diagnostic characters: Shell small and delicate, flattened; $3\frac{1}{2}$–$4\frac{1}{2}$ whorls; surface waxy crossed by strongly radiating striations, reddish-brown; umbilicus rather narrow; animal grey and head bluish-black.

Habitat: Widespread but local throughout British Isles in damp localities in meadows, marsh and woodland, amongst moss and at the bases of plants.

Retinella pura (Alder)

Height: 2 mm; *Breadth:* 4 mm.

Diagnostic characters: Shell very small, generally similar to *R. radiatula*, but much paler and more transparent; 4 whorls; surface with fine transverse striations crossed by delicate spiral markings; wider umbilicus; animal pale whitish-yellow.

Habitat: Generally distributed in damp shady areas.

Retinella nitidula (Draparnaud)

Height: 3 mm; *Breadth:* 6·5 mm.

Diagnostic characters: Shell with slightly flared last whorl and a dull horny or waxy appearance; relatively strongly built; amber-coloured on upper surface, paler below; large eccentric umbilicus; animal grey or greyish-black.

Habitat: The commonest species of *Retinella*, general throughout British Isles, in woods, hedges, amongst leaves and under stones, and in marshes.

Zonitoides nitidus (Müller)

Height: 3 mm; *Breadth:* 6 mm.

Diagnostic characters: Shell small, depressed, but less so than the preceding species, with slightly more pronounced spire; $4\frac{1}{2}$–5 whorls, increasing only slowly; aperture tends to be inclined downwards, rounder than in species of *Retinella* and *Oxychilus* above; glossy, rather silky surface, but with prominent transverse striations; deep reddish-brown colour; animal blue-black, dark spot on mantle.

Habitat: Widely distributed, in very wet localities, (hygrophile species), river banks and marshes; the similar but less flattened *Z. excavatus* (Alder) (7 mm broad), with a wider umbilicus, is interesting in that it is the only British land snail known actually to avoid calcareous soils, i.e. it is a calcifuge species, mostly restricted to acid woods.

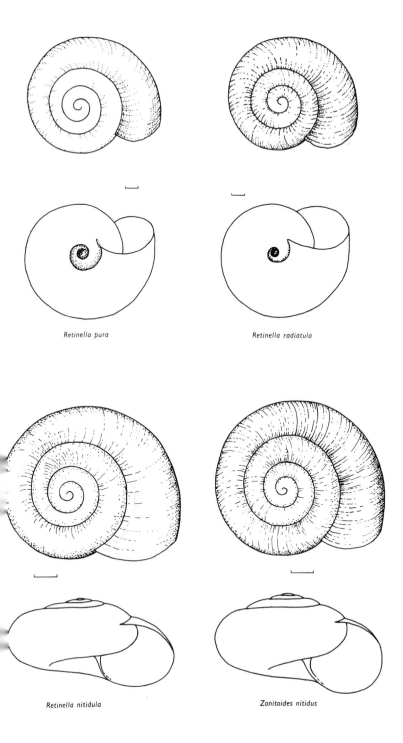

Retinella pura

Retinella radiatula

Retinella nitidula

Zonitoides nitidus

Vitrina pellucida (Müller)
Height: 3 mm; *Breadth:* 5 mm.

Diagnostic characters: Shell small and very fragile, delicate and translucent; $3\frac{1}{2}$ whorls, increasing rapidly, the body whorl being relatively broad and expanded; large downturned aperture at least half the breadth of the shell; glossy surface, greenish colour; animal grey, dark head.

Habitat: In leaves, moss, debris, under logs, in damp cool localities, also dry places (sandhills, chalk downs, etc.); almost ubiquitous.

General features: This snail, in which in the living animal the shell is partly enveloped by the mantle tissues, is representative of a group probably quite near to the ancestral stock leading to one family of the British terrestrial slugs, the Limacidae (see p. 136).

Slugs

Although it is convenient to deal with the terrestrial slugs in one section it should be stressed that they comprise three clearly defined families which were each evolved independently from different stocks of pulmonate snails. Identification of closely-related species is not easy on external features alone and may require examination of the internal anatomy. Full details and guides to the British slugs are given in works by Ellis and Quick (see Appendix).

Testacella haliotidea Draparnaud
Length (animal): Up to 120 mm; *Shell:* 7 × 5 mm.

Diagnostic characters: Animal bearing small external shell, brownish and somewhat convex, at posterior end of body; animal dull greyish-cream, pale sole to foot; tentacles not swollen at tip.

Habitat: In gardens, mostly underground; nocturnal, feeding on earthworms; generally distributed northwards to central Scotland; also parts of Ireland.

General features: Testacella typifies the shelled slugs (Testacellidae) characterised by the retention of an external, although very reduced, shell, and by their exclusively carnivorous habits. Their ancestors amongst the snails are not represented in the British fauna. There are two other species; *T. scutulum* Sowerby of similar size and distribution, with a dark-speckled yellowish body and a smaller flatter shell, and the smaller *T. maugei* Férussac, the most westerly species, distinguished by a larger ear-shaped shell (14 × 7 mm) and a brownish, black-sprinkled body.

Vitrina pellucida

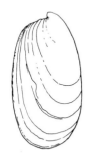

Testacella maugei—shell

Testacella scutulum—shell

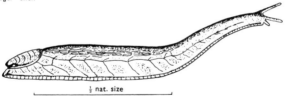

½ nat. size

Testacella haliotidea
(after Ellis)

Arion ater ater (L.)

Length: 140 mm.

Diagnostic characters: Animal large, variable colour but typically dark, black or brown and less commonly paler; shell reduced, internal and granular, covered by coarsely roughened mantle at front of body, respiratory opening placed forward on right-hand side; skin covering rounded keel-less body bears rows of elongated tubercles; characteristically the animal contracts into a hemispherical shape when disturbed, but may sway from side to side when gently touched; slime colourless.

Habitat: Widely distributed and common throughout the British Isles in all kinds of habitats, including open moorland, grassy areas, scrubland and woods.

General features: Arion ater typifies the Arionidae, probably originating from ancestors close to the Endodontidae family of snails (see p. 124). Arionid slugs have the respiratory opening generally placed anteriorly on the mantle, and the body lacks a keel. In addition to the large, typically black, form described here, there is a separate subspecies, *Arion ater rufus* (L.); this is commonly reddish in colour but is only distinguishable accurately from *A. a. ater* by examination of the reproductive system. It appears to show greater preference for cultivated areas, e.g. gardens and parks than the black form. Like other wild slugs with a reduced internal shell, most species of *Arion* show no obvious preference for calcareous or non-calcareous soils; indeed slugs can extend more easily into the latter than snails. *Arion ater* is an omnivorous species tackling most food including decaying animal and vegetable matter. Worth mentioning here is the unusual arionid slug, *Geomalacus maculosus* Allman, clearly distinguished by its spotted appearance. It is a Lusitanian species (see p. 122) restricted climatically to S.W. Ireland and found there only in Cork and Kerry.

Arion intermedius Normand

Length: 20 mm.

Diagnostic characters: Animal small, with steeply inclined back at rear end; yellowish-grey; characterised by prominent conical tubercles which stand out in the contracted state giving the surface a spiky appearance; slime yellow.

Habitat: Widely distributed in scrub, fields, marshes and woodland, associated with moist débris.

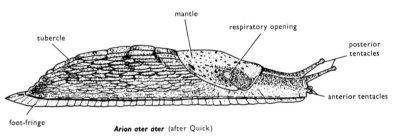

½ natural size

tubercle

mantle

respiratory opening

posterior
tentacles

anterior tentacles

foot-fringe

Arion ater ater (after Quick)

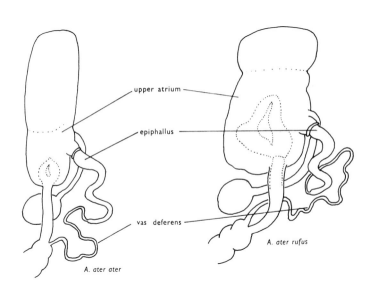

upper atrium

epiphallus

vas deferens

A. ater ater

A. ater rufus

Distal genital ducts (after Quick)

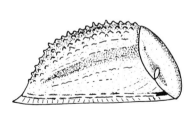

Arion intermedius

Arion hortensis Férussac

Length: 30 mm.

Diagnostic characters: Animal slender, dark-coloured, especially on back; grey to black with smaller paler dots; dark band down each side of the body, that on the right enclosing the respiratory opening; animal appears semi-circular in end-view when contracted; sole of foot yellow-orange, mucus from foot colourless, that from rest of body orange.

Habitat: Generally distributed and common in cultivated areas, including gardens, where it is a major pest; also occurs however in woods and other localities, under logs or in similar sheltered areas.

General features: This common garden slug causes much damage to cultivated crops. It burrows in the turned-over soil, eating rotting vegetation and the roots and lower stems of many important crop plants.

Arion circumscriptus Johnston [*A. fasciatus* Nilsson]

Length: 35 mm.

Diagnostic characters: This slug is regarded as an aggregate of three species; the type can be distinguished from *A. hortensis* by its greyish colour with darker band on each side, that on the right arching over, and not enclosing, the respiratory opening, by the characteristic bell-shaped appearance in end-view when contracted (see fig. opposite), and by the sole of the foot being a dull opaque white in colour; mucus colourless.

Habitat: Widely distributed in fields, hedges and woodlands, but also in gardens, feeding on rotting material and fungi.

Arion subfuscus (Draparnaud)

Length: 60 mm.

Diagnostic characters: Animal average-sized, yellowish- or dusky-brown, with darker lateral bands; does not appear hemispherical when contracted; sole of foot slightly translucent, yellowish-white; mucus from body yellow-orange, that from the foot colourless.

Habitat: Generally distributed in hedges and in woodlands under logs and litter or other shelter, occasionally in gardens; feeds on algal and fungal film on logs, also on larger fungi.

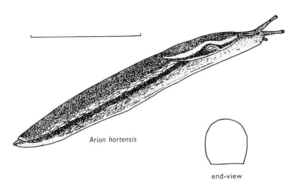

Arion hortensis

end-view

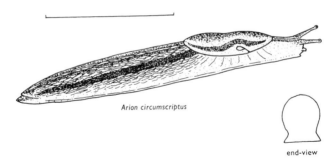

Arion circumscriptus

end-view

Arion subfuscus

Milax budapestensis (Hazay)

Length: 50 mm.

Diagnostic characters: Animal with mantle bearing a distinct pigmented furrow shaped like a horseshoe; body dark grey with long, prominent yellowish keel, respiratory opening posteriorly placed with a grey rim; sole of foot tripartite with median darker stripe; sticky mucus.

Habitat: Generally distributed, mainly in gardens and cultivated areas, where it burrows and is consequently a pest of roots and tubers.

General features: This slug introduces the Limacidae (Keelback slugs), a group which probably shares a common ancestry with snails similar to the *Vitrina* species described on p. 130. Limacid slugs all bear keeled bodies, and the respiratory opening lies towards the rear of the mantle. *M. budapestensis* is the commonest of *Milax* species. *M. sowerbyi* (Férussac) is also a garden root-crop pest, but more locally distributed; it is distinguished by its larger size (70 mm), uniformly pale sole to the foot and pale-rimmed respiratory opening. Somewhat rarer still is *M. gagates* (Draparnaud), uniformly dark in colour and lacking a pale margin to the respiratory aperture; although found in gardens, this species lives more naturally in wilder grassy localities, especially on the coast in south-western areas.

Limax maximus L.

Length: 150 mm.

Diagnostic characters: Animal large, various shades of grey, with two or three darker longitudinal bands down each side (sometimes as spots); concentrically ridged mantle, pointed posteriorly, with dark marbled pattern, hides flat, internal shell; long pointed tail with keel towards the rear; brown tentacles; pale foot; colourless mucus.

Habitat: Generally distributed in hedges and woods, and also in gardens, near houses; nocturnal, feeding on fungi and damp, rotting matter.

Limax flavus L.

Length: 85 mm.

Diagnostic characters: Animal greyish-yellow or greenish, colour partly due to the yellow mucus produced; mantle mottled with yellow or with yellow spots; not banded; tentacles steely blue colour.

Habitat: Found usually in gardens or associated with houses, particularly older property, and farm-buildings; an anthropophile species, almost domesticated in its habits, generally distributed but not so frequent in Scotland; common in Ireland; feeds on rubbish of all kinds.

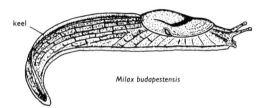

keel

Milax budapestensis

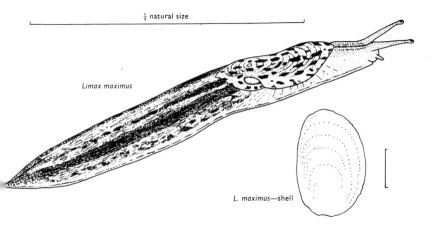

½ natural size

Limax maximus

L. maximus—shell

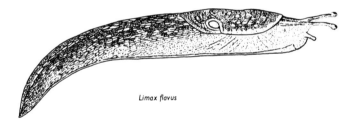

Limax flavus

Lehmannia marginata (Müller)

Length: 75 mm.

Diagnostic characters: Animal very soft and gelatinous with high water absorption potentiality; grey with paler band down the middle of the back including the keeled posterior end; 2 darker longitudinal bands on each side; mucus colourless.

Habitat: In woodlands mainly, also on rock surfaces, generally distributed; climbs trees, especially in wet conditions, where it feeds on encrusting lichens and fungi.

General features: This limacid slug is unusually soft-bodied and produces a watery mucus which can be drawn out into threads. By this means it can ascend or descend a tree, rather like a spider using a silk dragline. Mention might be made here of the similarly gelatinous but much smaller *Limax tenellus* Müller (30 mm long), pale yellow with dark head and tentacles, and the largest British slug, *Limax cinereoniger* Wolf, generally. black and 200 mm or more long; both are truly 'wild' (anthropophobe) species typically found in old woodlands.

Agriolimax reticulatus (Müller)

Length: 35 mm.

Diagnostic characters: Animal with mantle rounded at posterior as well as anterior end, nucleus of mantle ridges lies to right of mid-line; tail obliquely truncated in side view, not pointed (contrast *Limax* species); colour variable but usually buff with mottled or variegated darker markings; mucus is milky-white and stiffened with lime.

Habitat: Ubiquitous, common, and is a serious pest to crops in gardens and cultivated land; eats practically anything, and lives in a wide variety of wild habitats as well as in gardens; the closely-related but distinct species, *A. agrestis* (L.), smaller with a paler uniform colour, is found only very locally, e.g. in the fenlands of Norfolk, and parts of Scotland.

Agriolimax laevis (Müller)

Length: 20 mm.

Diagnostic characters: Animal small, glossy, coloured brown with darker spots; mantle paler and more centrally placed than other species; sole of foot pale brown; mucus colourless and clear.

Habitat: Widely distributed and frequent in wetter localities, e.g., marshes and river banks (hygrophile species), also in moist woodland; it has been recorded in greenhouses, but here one is more likely to find the larger, and much more active, *A. caruanae* Pollonera.

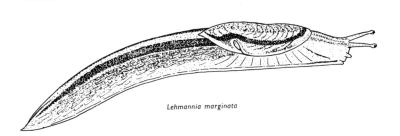

Lehmannia marginata

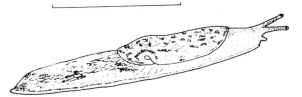

Agriolimax reticulatus

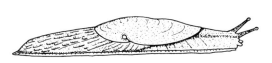

Agriolimax laevis

CLASS: SCAPHOPODA

Dentalium entalis (L.)   Tusk shell

Height: 34 mm; *Breadth:* 4 mm.

Diagnostic characters: Shell strong, glossy, tubular (open at both ends) and slightly curved; ivory-white and appearing like an elephant's tusk in shape.

Habitat: Burrows in sand off-shore, but shell may be washed up, more especially on northern coasts.

General features: This is perhaps the best-known of five British species of tusk-shells, representing a very small but interesting class of Mollusca, the Scaphopoda. They show in some ways an amalgam of features reminiscent of both the gastropods, and of the bivalves, described below. The animal lives buried in sand in deeper water, the narrower end of its characteristically-shaped shell projecting up into the water. It is through this opening that the respiratory current enters and leaves the mantle cavity. The foot protrudes through the broader end of the 'tusk' embedded deep in the sand. Through this opening also emerge some rather unusual retractile filaments attached to the head region; these pick minute, living shelled protozoa (foraminiferans) out of the surrounding substrate and transfer them to the mouth as food material.

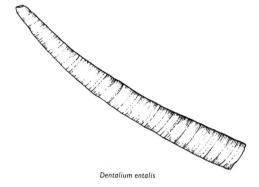

Dentalium entalis

CLASS: BIVALVIA

The bivalve molluscs, typified by the common mussels, are easily distinguishable by their shell, which as the name of the class indicates consists of two valves united along the upper (dorsal) edge by an elastic ligament (figs. 5 and 9). In the living animal the two valves are held close together by the adductor muscles and if these are cut, or cease to operate when the animal becomes moribund or dies, the valves spring open due to the natural elasticity of the ligament. Typically there are two such muscles, one anterior and one posterior, primitively equally developed as shown in fig. 7, constituting the isomyarian condition. In other bivalves, they may differ in size (heteromyarian) as seen in the mussel, *Mytilus*, where the anterior adductor is reduced, or consist

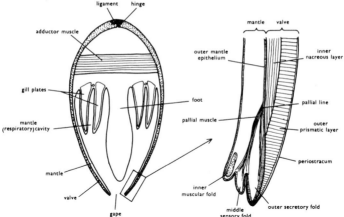

FIG. 5 Transverse section of a generalised bivalve

FIG. 6 More detailed view of the mantle and valve margin

of the posterior muscle only, the anterior muscle having been lost, lying almost centrally in a rounded shell (monomyarian condition), exemplified by the scallops (fig. 8). It is the antagonism operating between the adductor muscles on the one hand and the ligament on the other which enables the bivalve to adjust the degree to which the pair of valves open or gape during its various activities, for example, when burrowing. The hinge of the shell, i.e. the region in which the ligament is situated, may also bear a series of processes or depressions on the inside of the valves, constituting the hinge-teeth (fig. 10). These prevent the valves slipping or moving upon each other and where present the variation in their form and appearance may contribute significantly to the identification of different species.

The body of the bivalve is almost completely enclosed by the shell; the head region, so characteristic of the gastropods, is absent and there is no radula. The sensory functions of the head may be taken over by the sensory fold at the mantle edge (fig. 6), especially in the free-swimming scallops where it bears numerous tentacles and eyes. The foot is flattened laterally, a feature which is reflected in the name, Pelecypoda ('hatched-footed'), by which the bivalves are sometimes known. The blade-like foot can be protruded between the gape of the valves in many forms and used in burrowing or digging into sandy or muddy substrates, which are characteristic habitats of a wide range of bivalves. In others, however, like the common sea mussel, the foot is reduced but contains a glandular organ secreting a mass of tough, horny threads, constituting the byssus, by which the bivalve attaches itself to the rock surface.

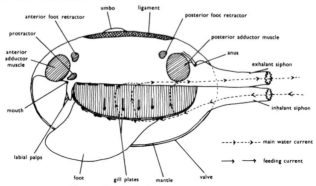

FIG. 7 Lateral view of a generalised bivalve with the left valve removed; this also demonstrates the Isomyarian condition

The compressed nature of the body, and the relatively sessile (static) or slow-moving way of live of the bivalve, is associated in most species with great enlargement of the gills down each side of their body and their adaptation as feeding organs (fig. 7). The extended and flattened gills (hence the name Lamellibranchia or 'leaf-gilled' applied to more advanced bivalves) sieve or filter out small food particles, usually of microscopic plant life, suspended in the surrounding water, these particles then being carried to the mouth by ciliary action. The mouth opening is guarded by flap-like structures, the labial palps, which help to sort the particles and reject unwanted material. The water from which the food is extracted is in fact swept through the gill chambers by the combined action of cilia on the gill surface, the main currents entering and leaving at the posterior end of the animal by way of the inhalant and exhalant openings respectively (fig. 7). The mantle here may be extended into tubes or siphons which enable the bivalve, when buried in the ground, often to appreciable depths, to maintain contact through the incoming (inhalant) and outgoing (exhalant) streams of water with its source of food supply. The variation in form shown by these siphons and the degree to which they can be extended can provide a useful guide to identification of many bivalves.

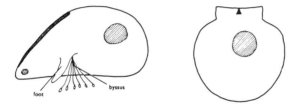

FIG. 8 Diagram showing (a) heteromyarian condition, with anterior adductor reduced, e.g. *Mytilus*, and(b) monomyarian condition, with single posterior adductor muscle remaining, e.g. *Pecten*

Inevitably, however, as in the snails, it is the shell in the bivalves which constitutes one of its most important diagnostic features. In addition to the position and form of the ligament, including, for example, whether it lies embedded mainly within the hinge region, i.e. internal in position, or whether it protrudes largely above the hinge-line, i.e. constituting an external ligament, structural features of the valves are important in identification (see figs. 9 and 10). The hinge of each valve commonly bears teeth, which interlock to maintain stability. These hinge teeth can be valuable diagnostic features. They may be numerous and similar in form (taxodont dentition), the primi-tive arrangement (see figs. facing p. 154), or fewer and dissimilar (heterodont dentition). In the latter case, the teeth may be centrally positioned near the umbones (cardinal teeth) and/or some distance anterior or posterior along the hinge (lateral teeth) (see fig. of *Mactra* facing p. 184).

The two valves are often similar in appearance, or equivalve; if dissimilar, as for example in the common scallop, *Pecten*, they are described as inequivalve. On the outer surface, the umbo (plural: umbones), situated at the uppermost or dorsal part of each valve, represents its centre of growth. The actual shape of the umbo, which may have a prominent terminal point, or beak, can be an important

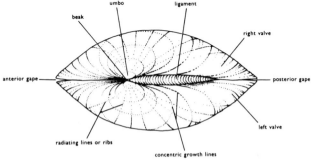

FIG. 9 View of a generalised bivalve from the upper (dorsal) aspect to show shell structure

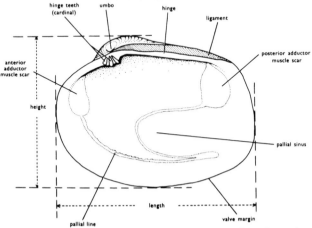

FIG. 10 View of the inside of the right valve of a generalised bivalve to show the main features used in identification

character in separating species. If growth occurs symmetrically around the umbones, which constitute the oldest parts of the valves, so that the anterior and posterior halves of the shell grow roughly equally in size, the valves are designated as equilateral. Where the front or rear portion of the shell is relatively larger, and the umbones do not lie centrally in the hinge-line, the valves are known as inequilateral. The outer surface of the valves, which is covered by the horny periostracum (fig. 6), is usually marked by concentric growth lines appearing as ridges or striations. Some may have ribs radiating from the umbo to the margin, as does the shell of the common cockle, *Cerastoderma [Cardium] edule*, whereas in other bivalves the outer surface may be comparatively smooth. In certain cases, as in many freshwater mussels, the periostracum may be worn away or eroded near the umbones, revealing the underlying calcareous layers of the shell, typically the outer prismatic layer shown in fig. 6.

The inner surface of the valves is usually smooth, composed in several bivalves largely of the inner nacreous layer of the shell, described because of its characteristic lustre, as 'mother-of-pearl'. The same material constitutes true pearls which are natural products of several bivalves, e.g. *Margaritifera* (see p. 196). The adductor muscles of the shell and the musculature of the foot form impressions or scars on the inner surface of the valves, which can vary appreciably in form, reflecting the isomyarian, heteromyarian and monomyarian conditions already described. The pallial muscles, which attach the mantle edge to the valves (fig. 6) leave a characteristic scar, the pallial line, joining the adductor muscle scars and running near the shell margin (fig. 10); this may form an inpushing or embayment, the pallial sinus, posteriorly, which is most evident in those bivalves which have long siphons and are deep burrowers.

The following keys for marine and freshwater bivalves use, as in the gastropods, a combination of characters based on habitat, shell morphology and general anatomy. They are similarly designed as a guide to identification of the relatively common species from both the major habitats described and illustrated in the ensuing pages. The sequence in which the species are treated is not intended to indicate evolutionary relationships; indeed, classification of the bivalves is not easy and is based on rather detailed features of the internal anatomy, including gill structure, and of the hinge region. A general classificatory scheme for the bivalves is given along with that of the other major groups in the Appendix.

Key to Marine Bivalvia

1. Hinge line usually extended into lateral processes or ears; ligament internal; surface of shell ribbed; single adductor muscle; empty shells commonly washed up on shore (Scallops and related forms)   2
   Hinge line without ears   7

2. Ears not prominent; whitish; wide gape   *Lima* spp. (p. 164)
   Ears prominent; shell frequently brightly coloured   3

3. Shell very large (120 mm long); valves dissimilar (inequivalve), the right (lower) valve rounded and the left (upper) valve flat
   Pecten maximus Great scallop (p. 162)
   Shell smaller; valves generally similar (equivalve), both convex

4. Valve outline distorted in adult; adult shell permanently cemented by right (lower) valve which becomes more convex   4
   with age ..   ..   *Chlamys distorta* (p. 164)
   Valve outline regular; adult shells not cemented   5

5. Ears generally similar in size, although variable; shell circular; 20 ribs; 55 mm diameter   ..   ..
   Chlamys opercularis Queen scallop (p. 162)
   Ears dissimilar, anterior ones much longer   6

6. Shell mainly oval; 28 rather spiny ribs; 40 mm long ..   ..
   Chlamys varia (p. 164)
   Shell half this size; finer sculpture; lower half of shell semicircular   ..   ..   *Chlamys tigerina* (p. 164)

7. Shell cemented to surface of rocks or stones, or very closely attached by limy byssus; valves generally rounded; inequivalve; single adductor muscle   8
   Shell not cemented; variably-shaped but usually with two adductor muscles   11

8. Shell thick and well-built with irregular surface; neither valve with hole; left valve convex and cemented to ground, right valve flat (True oysters) 9
   Shell smoother and less heavy; right (lower) valve pierced by hole through which passes a byssus impregnated with lime to attach animal closely to underlying surface (Saddle oysters) .. 10

9. Shell more or less circular; adductor muscle scar white ..
   Ostrea edulis Flat or edible oyster (p. 160)
   Shell much taller than broad; adductor muscle scar brown or purple .. .. .. *Crassostrea angulata* (p. 160)

10. Upper (imperforate) valve bears three separate muscle scars
    Anomia ephippium (p. 158)
    Upper valve with two separate muscle scars .. .. ..
    Monia patelliformis (p. 158)

11. Shell tiny, 3 mm long; oval, whitish with red tinge; in lichens, crevices and empty barnacle shells (with small gastropods, e.g. *Otina*, p. 74) .. .. *Lasaea rubra* (p. 166)
    (for these and several other very small bivalves, some associated with other animals, see p. 166)
    Shell larger 12

12. Shell mainly triangular with umbones at or near the relatively pointed anterior end; adductor muscles dissimilar, the anterior smaller than the posterior (heteromyarian); attached by byssus; no true siphons 13
    Shell otherwise shaped, and not usually attached to surface by byssus (see however *Arca*, certain *Venerupis* species and *Hiatella* below); mostly burrowers in sand or mud, or borers into rock or wood, with distinct siphons at posterior end .. 17

13. Shell very large, fan-shaped, 240 mm long (the largest British bivalve); empty shells may be found on shore .. .. ..
    Pinna fragilis (p. 158)
    Shell smaller (True mussels and related forms) 14

14. Shell pointed anteriorly, umbones terminal; bluish-black; one of the commonest bivalves on rocky shores.

Mytilus edulis Common mussel (p. 156)

Shell less pointed at anterior end, with umbones not at the tip but on upper surface.   15

15. Shell small, 10 mm long, greenish or .. yellow-brown   *Musculus discors* (p. 158)
Shell often larger, darker, frequently with horny processes on outer surface (Horse mussels)   16

16. Large, over 100 mm long; dark purplish shell with processes on surface of young but not of adult stage ..   ..
                    Modiolus modiolus Horse mussel (p. 156)
Shell half this size and bears stiff, thorn-like serrated processes over posterior half   ..   *Modiolus barbatus* (p. 156)
Smaller still, 10 mm long; processes from shell not serrated; bean-shaped shell   ..   *Modiolus phaseolinus* (p. 156)

17. Burrowers into mud or sand*   18
Wood or rock borers   47

18. Shell with numerous small teeth along the hinge line (taxodont dentition)   19
Hinge not taxodont   20

*It may not always be easy to ascertain habitats directly from shells, but, in general, shells of wood or rock borers tend to be located in their own natural environment or often reduced or much modified. Most other shells, if not already keyed out, may be taken to be burrowers in muddy or sandy substrates.

19. Shell rather triangular and bears hinge teeth arranged in comb-like rows on either side of an internal ligament; off-shore species .. .. *Nucula* spp. (p. 154)
Shell almost circular with external ligament lying above and not between the hinge teeth; characteristic brownish markings; only on shore when washed up as empty shells .. ..
Glycymeris glycymeris (p. 154)
Shell boat-shaped with broad external ligament also lying above a continuous row of hinge teeth; lies attached by large green byssus in rock crevices on shore as well as in deeper water .. .. *Arca tetragona* (p. 154)

20. Shell very large, almost 100 mm diameter, roughly circular, heavy and dark brown; lives off-shore but empty shells seen quite frequently on beaches .. *Arctica islandica* (p. 166)
Shell otherwise shaped or smaller 21

21. Shell globular and swollen (heart-shaped end-view); shallow burrowers with short siphons; no pallial sinus 22
Shell less swollen; pallial sinus commonly present 25

22. Shell surface smooth; very curved inrolled umbones; almost 90 mm diameter; off-shore species *Glossus humanus* (p. 166)
Shell surface usually with conspicuous radial ribs (True cockles) 23

23. Ribs weakly developed giving shell relatively smooth appearance; off-shore species .. *Laevicardium crassum* (p. 168)
Ribs prominent 24

24. Shell 45 mm across, occasionally larger, with 22–28 ribs; furrows extend from ridged margin a short way inside shell (approximately to pallial line); abundant on sandy shores ..
Cerastoderma [*Cardium*] *edule* Common cockle (p. 168)
Shell larger, 55 mm across, with 18–20 ribs bearing sharp spines which tend to point towards rear of shell; furrows extend much further inside shell; mainly off-shore .. .. ..
Acanthocardia echinata (p. 168)
Shell much smaller, 16 mm across, with 20–22 ribs, some bearing small processes (tubercles); no internal furrows; more common off-shore than inter-tidally .. ..
Parvicardium exiguum (p. 168)

25. Shell solid, often coloured, with umbones curved inwards and
    turned towards the anterior end (Venerids) 26
    Umbones not anteriorly directed 32

26. Shell with characteristic heart-
    shaped lunule in front of umbo;
    valves rounded or triangular .. 27
    Shell with less obvious lunule;
    rhomboid-shaped, umbones much
    nearer anterior end 30

27. Interior border of valves smooth; shell rounded .. ..
                                          Dosinia spp. (p. 170)
    Interior border of valves notched or serrated; shell more
    triangular in shape 28

28. Shell large, 75 mm long; rough, irregular patch on hinge
    beneath ligament .. *Mercenaria mercenaria* (p. 172)
    Shell smaller; no rough patch beneath ligament 29

29. Shell with three reddish-brown rays radiating from hinge to
    margin of valves; numerous narrow concentric ridges; liga-
    ment visible when valves closed; 30 mm long .. .. ..
                                          Venus striatula (p. 170)
    Shell with a few broad, flattened concentric ridges; variably
    but often brightly coloured; ligament almost hidden when
    valves closed; 20 mm across   *Venus fasciata* (p. 172)
    Shell with raised, sharply-edged concentric ridges; usually
    whitish but may have reddish-brown radiating markings;
    45 mm long; common off-shore species   *Venus casina* (p. 172)
    (for these and other *Venus* species see p. 172)

30. Shell rather glossy with mainly concentric ridges and usually
    lacking radial lines .. .. *Venerupis rhomboides* (p. 174)
    Shell less glossy with radiating lines as well as concentric
    markings 31

31. Shell with fine sculpture and strong brown or purplish mark-
    ings .. .. .. *Venerupis pullastra* (p. 174)
    Shell with prominent criss-cross sculpture giving surface
    decussate or cross-grained appearance .. .. ..
                                          Venerupis decussata (p. 174)
    Shell small, distorted; concentric ridges marked posteriorly;
    in rock crevices attached by byssus   *Venerupis saxatilis* (p. 176)

32. Shell generally thin and flattened, often with prominent external ligament (see however *Scrobicularia*, 35, below); valves may be twisted towards posterior end; siphons long and separate 33
   Shell otherwise shaped; siphons short or long, but if the latter, fused and covered by a horny sheath 36

33. Ligament prominent and completely external 34
   Ligament partly external and partly internal 35

34. Very thin, flattened, pinkish or white shell; length (up to 22 mm) exceeds height; in sand, common on shore .. ..
   Tellina tenuis (p. 178)
   (*T. fabula* similar, but right valve bears diagonal striations; mainly off-shore species.)
   Shell more globular and rounded; length (up to 20 mm) almost equal to height; on shore, in muddy sand .. ..
   Macoma balthica (p. 178)
   Shell more solid and larger (up to 50 mm long); prominent concentric ridges; off-shore species   *Tellina crassa* (p. 178)

35. Shell large (up to 45 mm long) and well-built; usually light brownish-yellow; siphons extremely long; in mud, both shore and estuaries   .. ..   *Scrobicularia plana* (p. 180)
   Shell thinner, smaller (20 mm or less); white; common off-shore bivalve, in mud .. .. ..   *Abra* spp. (p. 180)

36. Shell greatly elongated, much longer than it is tall; razor-shaped 37
   Shell not razor-shaped 39

37. Umbones and ligament central .. .. *Pharus legumen* (p. 180)
   Umbones and ligament at the anterior end (True razor shells) 38

38. Shell long and straight, ends square-cut; reaching 200 mm ..
   Ensis siliqua (p. 182)
   Shell shorter (up to 150 mm), slightly curved; posterior end slightly tapered .. .. *Ensis arcuatus* (p. 182)
   Shell shorter still (100 mm long) and markedly curved; posterior end appreciably tapered .. ..*Ensis ensis* (p. 182)

39. Shell markedly inequivalve, the right valve being much more cupped than the left; relatively small (13 mm); mainly off-shore   ..   ..   *Corbula gibba* (p. 188)
   Shell equivalve or only slightly inequivalve   40

40. Shell large (except for *Mya truncata*, 42, below, 100 mm or more long) and broadly oval with marked posterior gape; deep pallial sinus; long fused siphons covered by horny sheath   ..   41
   Shell smaller, with gape less marked or absent; short siphons   43

41. Ligament partly external; spoon-shaped pit (chondrophore) in both valves; shell equivalve ..   ..   *Lutraria* spp. (p. 186)
   Ligament mostly internal; large spoon-shaped process (chondrophore) in left valve only; right valve more swollen than left (True gapers)   42

42. Shell oval and large (100 mm long)   *Mya arenaria* (p. 186)
   Shell blunt posteriorly (truncated) and shorter (50 mm)   ..
                                             Mya truncata (p. 186)

43. Shell mostly triangular, equilateral; central hinge (cardinal) teeth have characteristic $\wedge$-shaped appearance in left valve (Trough shells)   44
   Shell more elongated, oval or wedge-shaped; without $\wedge$-shaped hinge teeth   45

44. Shell with brownish rays radiating from umbones; rather brittle; lateral hinge teeth smooth   *Mactra corallina* (p. 184)
   Shell off-white, without rays; more solid; lateral hinge teeth finely ridged   ..   ..   ..   *Spisula* spp. (p. 184)

45. Shell inequilateral with anterior part larger than the posterior; variably-coloured but inner surface usually with violet blotches; highly polished surface   *Donax vittatus* (p. 176)
   Shell nearly equilateral   46

46. Shell oval, no keel although slightly extended posteriorly; creamy-white with purple or pinkish rays radiating from the hinge   ..   ..   *Gari depressa* (p. 176)
   Shell more oblong with prominent posterior keel   ..   ..
                                             Gari fervensis (p. 176)

47. Typically rock borers 48
    Usually borers in wood 50

48. Shell generally oblong with irregular surface; prominent external ligament; bores in soft rock or may nestle in crevices; attached by byssus .. .. *Hiatella arctica* (p. 188)
    Shell cut away at front; commonly bears tubercles or spines on outer surface to aid in burrowing; with 1–4 accessory plates; ligament reduced or absent (piddocks) 49

49. Shell elongate, 100 mm long, hard but brittle, with 40–50 rows of spines; four accessory plates .. ..
    Pholas dactylus Common piddock (p. 188)
    Shell oval, smaller, divided into anterior and posterior portions by central furrow; anterior region with 20 rows of spines .. .. *Zirfaea crispata* (p. 190)
    Shell elongate, rather delicate, without furrow; chalky white; 25–30 longitudinal rows of spines; one accessory plate ..
    Barnea candida (p. 190)
    (*B. parva* has a more solid shell, also white but often stained reddish-brown from boring; (for these and other rock-borers, see p. 190)

50. Shell very reduced; body elongated and worm-like and cannot be withdrawn into shell; holes bored in wood can be closed by limy plugs or 'pallets'. .. *Teredo* spp. (p. 192)
    Shell surrounds body completely; no pallets .. .. ..
    Xylophaga dorsalis (p. 192)

Nucula sulcata Bronn

Length: 18 mm; *Height:* 14 mm.

Diagnostic characters: Shell small, triangular, with a row of numerous small teeth along each side of the hinge (taxodont condition), separated by a pit-like chondrophore bearing an internal ligament; matt outer surface bearing a fine criss-cross sculpture; shell margin ridged internally; olive-brown, sometimes stained deeper brown marginally; no pallial sinus.

Habitat: Widely distributed on muddy substrates off-shore.

General features: This is the largest of several British species of *Nucula*, members of a primitive group of bivalves, the Protobranchia, mainly found in deeper waters. Unlike the Lamellibranchia, constituting the remainder of the bivalves described below, the protobranchs do not have plate-like gills and are not suspension feeders. Instead, they use special elongated palps to collect food particles deposited on the sea bed. The related *Nuculana minuta* (Müller) is distinguished by a posterior keel-like process to the shell.

Glycymeris glycymeris (L.)

Length: 50 mm; *Height:* 48 mm.

Diagnostic characters: Shell thick, almost symmetrical and circular; valves equivalve and equilateral; hinge broad and bears a row of approximately 12 small teeth (taxodont) with smooth central area, all beneath the ligament; reddish-brown, often zig-zag markings on pale background; adductor muscle scars almost equal; no pallial sinus.

Habitat: Buried just beneath the surface of sand or gravel off-shore, although empty valves may be washed up; widely distributed.

General features: This species and *Arca* below are primitive representatives of the true lamellibranch bivalves, which so characterise the surface (epi-) fauna and burrowing (in-) fauna of the sea bed. These early forms demonstrate taxodont dentition and are typically surface dwellers, often attached by a byssus, or shallow burrowers.

Arca tetragona Poli

Length: 37 mm; *Height:* 20 mm.

Diagnostic characters: Shell boat-like, supposedly resembling Noah's ark; umbones anteriorly placed and wide apart; 40–50 small hinge teeth (taxodont) in continuous row beneath external ligament; yellowish, although often with darker markings; greenish byssus.

Habitat: Extreme low water and off-shore, attached by large byssus to rocks, shells or stones, often in crevices; generally distributed.

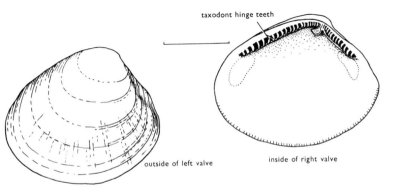

taxodont hinge teeth

outside of left valve

inside of right valve

Nucula sulcata

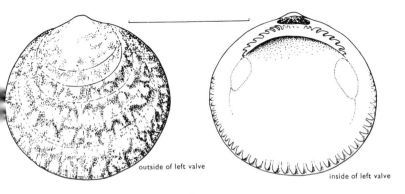

outside of left valve

inside of left valve

Glycymeris glycymeris

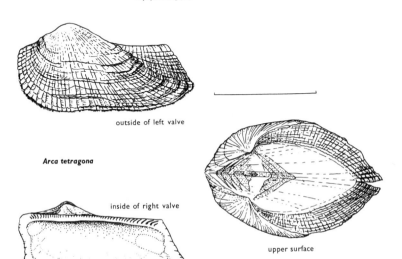

outside of left valve

Arca tetragona

inside of right valve

upper surface

Mytilus edulis L.   Common mussel

Length: 80 mm; *Height:* 45 mm.

Diagnostic characters: Shell almost triangular in outline with umbones at anterior pointed tip; dark blue-black; anterior adductor small, posterior adductor large (heteromyarian); well developed byssus.

Habitat: Widely distributed on all rocky shores, and indeed in all regions, including estuaries, where hard surfaces for byssus attachment occur; may form dense beds; middle and lower shore, abundant.

General features: Mytilus typifies the mussels or Mytilidae and is one of the most successful and prolific shore bivalves. It resists wave action by being firmly attached to rocks by the byssus threads. Mussels collected for food from commercial beds are carefully purified before marketing, a necessary procedure since the efficient filter-feeding mussels may harbour pathogenic bacteria, such as those causing typhoid, and other toxic substances which are increasingly polluting estuaries and coastal waters. The so-called Mediterranean mussel, *M. galloprovincialis* Lamarck, recorded on south-west coasts, characterised by turned-down umbones and a dark mantle edge, is probably only a variety of *M. edulis.*

Modiolus modiolus (L.)   Horse mussel

Length: 110 mm; *Height:* 55 mm.

Diagnostic characters: Shell large, solid, with umbones on upper surface a short way from the anterior end; purplish surface, drawn out in young forms into long smooth processes.

Habitat: Lower shore, amongst *Laminaria* holdfasts, or in rock pools, but more frequent and larger off-shore; widely distributed but more common in the north.

Modiolus barbatus (L.)

Length: 50 mm; *Height:* 27 mm.

Diagnostic characters: Shell thinner and roughly triangular; brownish periostracum drawn out into thorn-like serrated processes especially on posterior half of the shell.

Habitat: Under rocks and in *Laminaria* holdfasts, on low-water mark and below; widely distributed but more often in south and west.

Modiolus phaseolinus (Philippi)

Length: 10 mm; *Height;* 6 mm.

Diagnostic characters: Shell fragile, shaped like a small bean; yellow-purple colour; surface drawn out into long, but non-serrated, spines.

Habitat: On rocky ground, low water and below; widely distributed.

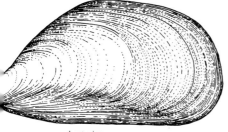

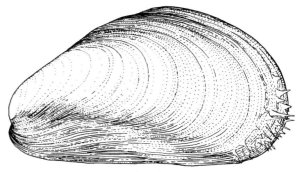

$\frac{1}{2}$ nat. size

Mytilus edulis

$\frac{1}{2}$ nat. size

Modiolus modiolus

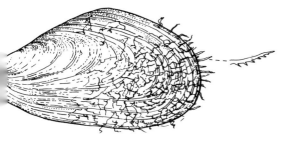

Modiolus barbatus

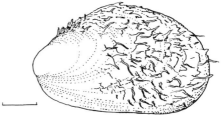

Modiolus phaseolinus

Musculus discors (L.)

Length: 10 mm; *Height:* 6 mm.

Diagnostic characters: Shell brittle, more rhomboid-shaped; yellow-brown with greenish periostracum; surface with radiating ribs.

Habitat: Under rocks, in pools or amongst corallines and other weeds; widely distributed, inter-tidal or deeper; the larger *M. marmoratus* (Forbes) may be found embedded in sea-squirts or amongst *Laminaria* holdfasts.

Pinna fragilis Pennant

Length: 240 mm; *Height:* 110 mm.

Diagnostic characters: Shell very large, brittle, fan-shaped with umbones at pointed anterior end; brownish colour; byssus.

Habitat: At low-water mark, or more usually off-shore, with pointed end buried in gravel, attached to rocks or stones beneath the surface by its well developed byssus; occurs around the British Isles but more often off the south coast.

General features: This species, popularly named the fan mussel but more highly evolved than the true mussels, is by far the largest British bivalve. It is, however, much more abundant in the Mediterranean where the long, rather silky byssus threads have long been used for weaving into fabrics and clothes.

Anomia ephippium L.

Length: 35 mm; *Height:* 35 mm.

Diagnostic characters: Shell generally circular, flattened, dull white but shiny inside; inequivalve, right (lower) valve thin and pierced by a hole (embayment) through which passes a limy byssus attaching the animal to the underlying surface (*Anomia*, the so-called saddle oyster, is therefore more closely related to the byssal-attached mussels than the truly cemented oysters—see *Ostrea* below); left (upper) valve more convex and solid, bearing three separate muscle scars, one from the single adductor and two from byssus muscles (contrast other British species, *Heteranomia* and *Monia*, see figs. opposite).

Habitat: On shells and undersurfaces of rocks at low water and below; widely distributed.

Monia patelliformis (L.)

Length: 25 mm; *Height:* 25 mm.

Diagnostic characters: Shell also flat, but unlike *Anomia*, left (upper) valve has only two separate muscle scars on inner surface.

Habitat: More frequent off-shore attached to rocks or hard surfaces

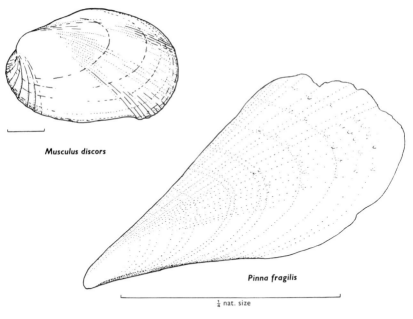

Musculus discors

Pinna fragilis

¼ nat. size

Anomia ephippium —outside of right
(lower) valve

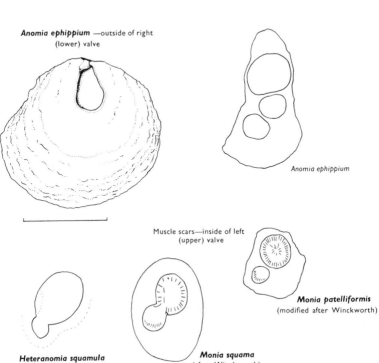

Anomia ephippium

Muscle scars—inside of left
(upper) valve

Monia patelliformis
(modified after Winckworth)

Heteranomia squamula

Monia squama
(after Winckworth)

Ostrea edulis L.   European, flat or edible oyster

Length: 90 mm; *Height:* 100 mm.

Diagnostic characters: Shell solid, thick, more or less circular but irregular shape; yellowish-brown; inequivalve, left (lower) valve convèx and right (upper) valve flat; single adductor muscle (monomyarian) leaves a white scar.

Habitat: Low-water mark to off-shore, where can form thick beds in creeks, estuaries and sheltered water on hard substrates; valves washed up, often bored by sponges; widely distributed, more especially in the south-east and south-west.

General features: This is one of the best-known bivalves, regarded now as a luxury choice amongst the edible species of molluscs, but at one time considered a staple food item. The animal is cemented to the ground by its rounded (left) valve, the attachment actually occurring after the larva (spat) has settled on a suitable surface and lost its temporary byssus. Cultivation of the major oyster beds, found particularly off south-eastern and south-western counties, is stimulated by providing clean shell or cultch for settlement of the spat. Overfishing, disease, pollution, the activity of predators including *Urosalpinx* (see p. 54) and the starfish, and competition with *Crepidula* (p. 48) have all contrived to reduce stocks of the native oyster, but experiments are being conducted at Government Fishery Laboratories on experimental rearing of oysters and control of pests with a view to improving and restocking natural beds. Oyster cultivation in other countries, for example, France, is on a much larger commercial scale.

Crassostrea angulata (Lamarck)

Length: 65 mm; *Height:* 100 mm.

Diagnostic characters: Shell much taller than broad and with left (lower) valve more cup-shaped than *Ostrea edulis*; margin folded; off-white, occasionally blotched; adductor muscle scar deep brown or purplish.

Habitat: An introduced species (so-called 'Portuguese oyster') which breeds in the south-east in shallow water, e.g. at Whitstable, in hot summers; the imported American oyster, *C. virginica* Gmelin, similar in shape but with a smoother margin, does not spawn here and is not regarded therefore as a member of the British fauna.

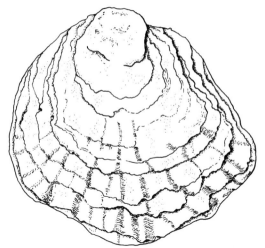

Ostrea edulis—right upper valve

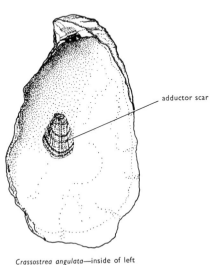

adductor scar

Crassostrea angulata—inside of left
lower valve

Pecten maximus (L.)   Great scallop

Length: 120 mm; *Height:* 110 mm.

Diagnostic characters: Shell well-built, large, almost circular, with equal processes (ears) adjoining hinge; right (lower) valve convex and left (upper) valve flat; 15–17 wide radiating ridges; yellow or reddish-brown; single adductor muscle.

Habitat: Mainly off-shore, swimming or resting on right convex valve; shells commonly washed up on shore, occasionally whole animals at low-water mark; widely distributed.

General features: This, the largest member of the family Pectinidae or scallops is edible and is fished commercially, mainly in the winter and early spring, by dredging in parts of the Channel, and especially in the Irish Sea, and off Western Scottish coasts. In its early life the scallop is attached by a byssus, a feature which links it evolutionarily with the Mytilidae, but later it loses the byssus and becomes free-swimming. The single, centrally-placed adductor muscle, derivable from the larger posterior adductor of the heteromyarian bivalve, is modified to carry out the rapid contractions necessary for swimming. It is composed of a large proportion of striated (striped) muscle fibres, functionally similar to those concerned with locomotion in the vertebrates, comprising the so-called 'quick' muscle. The remainder, constituting the 'catch' muscle, consist of unstriated fibres, which, as in other bivalves, hold the valves tightly together. The scallop's freedom of movement is reflected in the development of sensory tentacles and conspicuous bluish-green eyes along the mantle edge.

Chlamys opercularis (L.)   Queen scallop

Length: 55 mm; *Height:* 55 mm.

Diagnostic characters: Shell strong, circular, ears nearly equal; both valves convex, but inequivalve, the left (upper) valve more swollen than the right (lower) valve; approximately 20 rounded diverging ribs; colour variable.

Habitat: Mainly off-shore on firm sand or gravel, but occasionally washed up whole, or more frequently as empty shells; widely distributed; actively fished off western Scotland.

General features: This is one of the most active swimmers amongst British scallops, movement being accomplished by the rapid clapping together of the valves. Similar in shape but smaller and with far fewer ribs (3–10, typically 7) is *C. septemradiata* (Müller), best known from the Clyde Sea area.

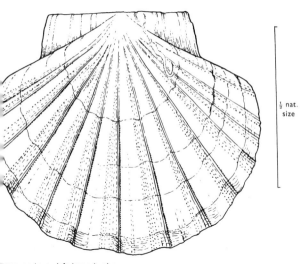

cten maximus—left (upper) valve

$\frac{1}{2}$ nat. size

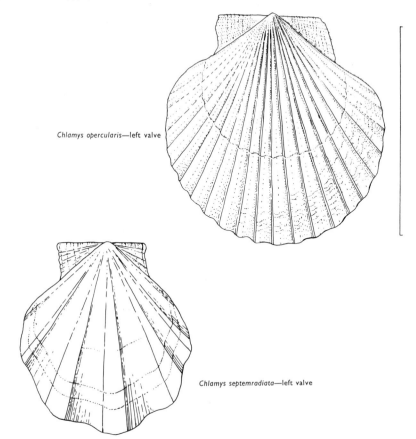

Chlamys opercularis—left valve

Chlamys septemradiata—left valve

Chlamys varia (L.)

Length: 28 mm; *Height:* 32 mm.

Diagnostic characters: Shell more oval than *C. opercularis*, with very unequal ears; 25–35 ribs, which bear spines near the margin; colour very variable.

Habitat: Low-water mark and below, free-moving or attached by byssus; widely distributed.

Chlamys distorta (da Costa)

Length: 35 mm; *Height:* 40 mm.

Diagnostic characters: Shell irregular and distorted in adult; ears dissimilar; 60–70 ribs bearing scaly spines in full-grown shell; variably patterned.

Habitat: Permanently cemented by lower right valve on rocky coasts at extreme low water and below; generally distributed.

Chlamys tigerina (Müller)

Length: 15 mm; *Height:* 16 mm.

Diagnostic characters: Shell small with asymmetrical ears; variable in sculpturing and colour, although usually finely-ribbed sometimes with characteristic 'tiger' pattern; lower half of shell semicircular.

Habitat: May occur low on shore, but more frequent in deeper waters; widely distributed around the British Isles.

Lima hians (Gmelin)

Length: 23 mm; *Height:* 34 mm.

Diagnostic characters: Shell whitish, oval, taller than broad with ears not well defined; 50 close-set ribs giving surface file-like appearance (hence popular name 'File-shell'); wide gape through which in life the mantle tissues protrude.

Habitat: Found in holes or crevices between rocks and in *Laminaria* holdfasts mainly beyond low water; more frequent off north-west coasts.

General features: This bivalve, perhaps the best known of the five British species of *Lima*, is characterised in life by its beautifully coloured, red and orange, tentacular mantle tissues. Closely related to the scallops, *L. hians* is relatively sedentary, and lives in a unique nest constructed from byssus threads which protects it whilst feeding.

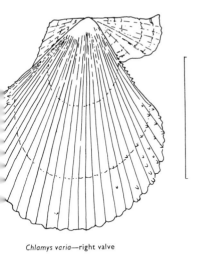

Chlamys varia—right valve

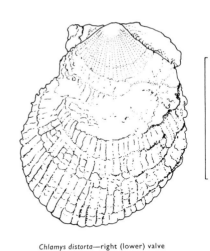

Chlamys distorta—right (lower) valve

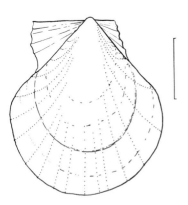

Chlamys tigerina—left valve

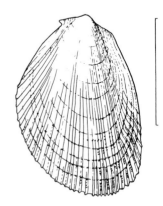

Lima hians—left valve

Lasaea rubra (Montagu)

Length: 3 mm; *Height:* 2 mm.

Diagnostic characters: Shell tiny, brittle, oval in shape; white tinged with red; concentrically ridged surface; byssus.

Habitat: Widely distributed inter-tidally on rocky shores in crevices, empty barnacles, shells and amongst weeds and tufts of lichens.

General features: This very small shell might be regarded as representative of a number of tiny bivalves found on British coasts. *Lasaea* is free-living, as also is the larger (10 mm) *Kellia suborbicularis* (Montagu) with a swollen white glossy shell more frequently found off-shore inside dead shells. Others, however, quite closely related, are associated (commensal) with other animals. Some of the best known are species of *Montacuta* with tiny pale shells found living with burrowing sea or heart-urchins, and the rather rare *Lepton squamosum* (Montagu), with small (10–12 mm) fragile, squarish white valves, between which in life project delicate white tentacular processes of the mantle, living associated with *Upogebia*, a burrowing shrimp, on southern coasts.

Arctica [Cyprina] islandica (L.)

Length: 95 mm; *Height:* 90 mm.

Diagnostic characters: Shell large, well-built and heavy; generally oval to circular with umbones pointing forwards; prominent external ligament; dark-brown; no pallial sinus.

Habitat: Widely distributed off-shore around the British Isles on sand or muddy sand.

General features: This big, unmistakable shell, a shallow burrower in deeper waters, is not unfrequently washed up as empty valves on the beach. Worth mentioning here also is another off-shore bivalve with similar habits, *Astarte*, comprising a group of five species, all with much smaller (mostly 25 mm or less), rather well built, triangular shells, concentrically ridged and all lacking a pallial sinus.

Glossus humanus (L.)

Length: 82 mm; *Height:* 75 mm.

Diagnostic characters: Shell large, heart-shaped in end-view, with markedly curved, inrolled umbones; brownish; no pallial sinus.

Habitat: Another large, off-shore shell, burrowing just beneath the surface in muddy sand, mainly off western and south-western coasts.

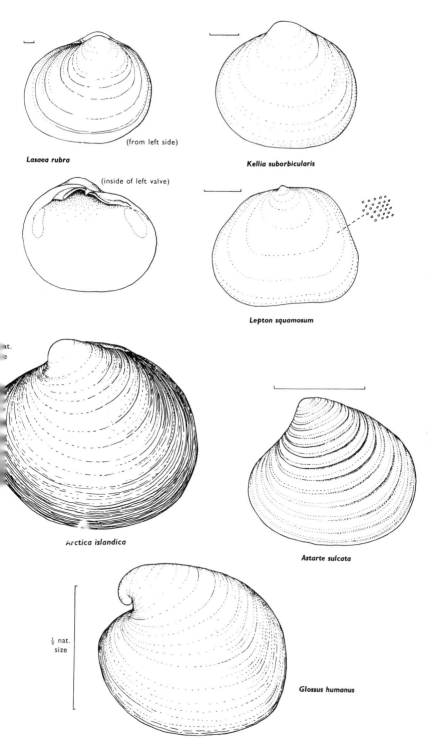

Lasaea rubra (from left side)

(inside of left valve)

Kellia suborbicularis

Lepton squamosum

½ nat.
size

Arctica islandica

Astarte sulcata

½ nat. size

Glossus humanus

Cerastoderma [***Cardium***] ***edule*** (L.)   Common or edible cockle

Length: 45 mm; *Height:* 40 mm.

Diagnostic characters: Shell solid, globular, umbones turned over; 22–28 prominent radiating ribs crossing fine concentric ridges; inside of shell margin ridged as far as pallial line; off-white, yellowish or brown; external ligament well marked; short siphons.

Habitat: Shallow burrower in clean sand or muddy sand; middle and lower shore; widely distributed; very common.

General features: The edible common cockle, best known member of the family Cardiidae, is a true shore animal and can, in suitable conditions, occur in enormous numbers in dense beds beneath the surface of sand, reaching a density of 10,000 specimens per sq. metre. In such areas the cockles are raked out of the sand and sold for food on a commercial scale. The cockle uses its large, powerful and angled foot not only for burrowing into the soft substrate by a series of co-ordinated digging movements, a habit to which most bivalves are adapted, but also for 'leaping' along the surface to escape its predators, particularly the starfish.

Acanthocardia echinata (L.)

Length: 55 mm; *Height:* 52 mm.

Diagnostic characters: Shell well-built with 18–20 ribs each bearing a row of sharp spines which tend to point posteriorly; marginal furrows extend a long way inside the shell.

Habitat: Widely distributed in sandy or other substrates, but more frequent off-shore; with similar habits but restricted to the south-west, are the even larger cockles, *A. aculeata* (L.) with a spiny shell and a characteristic red foot, and *A. tuberculata* (L.), a heavy shell with a coarse, tubercled surface.

Laevicardium crassum (Gmelin)

Length: 48 mm; *Height:* 50 mm.

Diagnostic characters: Shell similar in general to other cockles but with 40–50 ill-defined ribs giving surface an almost smooth appearance.

Habitat: Widely distributed in gravelly sand in deeper water.

Parvicardium exiguum (Gmelin)

Length: 16 mm; *Height:* 13 mm.

Diagnostic characters: Shell small, obliquely-angled, with 20–22 ribs, some bearing small tubercles; shell without internal furrows.

Habitat: Generally distributed in sand or muddy sand, mainly off-shore (several other species of small cockles also occur here).

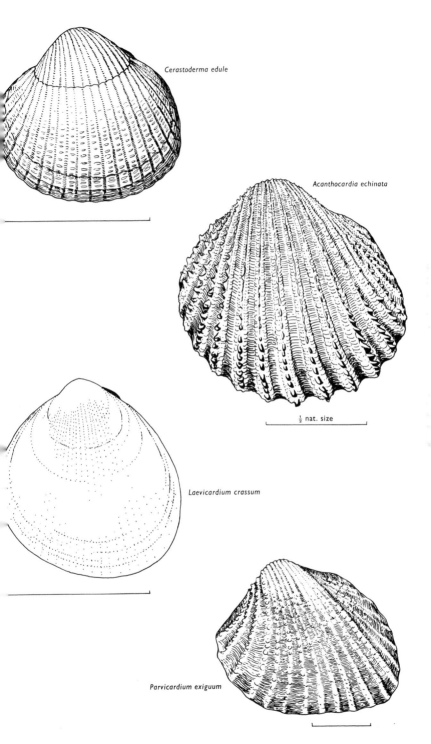

Cerastoderma edule

Acanthocardia echinata

½ nat. size

Laevicardium crassum

Parvicardium exiguum

Dosinia exoleta (L.)

Length: 47 mm; *Height:* 45 mm.

Diagnostic characters: Shell solid, nearly circular, with umbones curved inwards and turned towards anterior end; well defined heart-shaped lunule in front of umbo; curvature of shell anterior to lunule obvious; smooth interior margin to valves; well-marked concentric ridges on surface; off-white with brown or reddish rays or variegated markings; triangular pallial sinus extends deeply into shell.

Habitat: In sand, on lower shore downwards, mainly in sheltered bays; widely distributed.

General features: This and the following group of species comprise the large and successful bivalve family, Veneridae, including *Dosinia* (the artemis), venus and carpet shells. They have strong, often handsomely sculptured and coloured shells, and are active, often quite deep, burrowers. Two other rounded shells with forward-facing umbones might be mentioned here, both however from other bivalve families. These are *Lucinoma* [*Phacoides*] *borealis* (L.), with a white, concentrically ridged shell, and the smaller *Diplodonta rotundata* (Montagu), with a squarer, glossier shell. Both shells are, however, clearly distinguished from *Dosinia*, and indeed other venerids, by, for example, lack of a pallial sinus and of a distinct lunule.

Dosinia lupinus (L.)

Length: 28 mm; *Height:* 27 mm.

Diagnostic characters: Resembles *D. exoleta* in general shape, but is smaller, smoother and less obviously ridged, and lacks rays and other markings; curvature of the shell anterior to the lunule is low.

Habitat: Widely distributed in sand, from extreme low-water mark.

Venus striatula (da Costa)

Length: 30 mm; *Height:* 25 mm.

Diagnostic characters: Shell solid, thick, rather triangular with forwardly directed umbones; interior border of valves serrated; lunule short and heart-shaped; pale colour background but with three reddish-brown rays radiating from the umbones; ligament visible when valves closed; pallial sinus not deep.

Habitat: In sandy ground, lower shore and below; widely distributed.

General features: This is perhaps the commonest representative of the distinctive venus shells or clams which so successfully colonise British coasts. Their shells are distinguished from other venerids by the ridged inner margin.

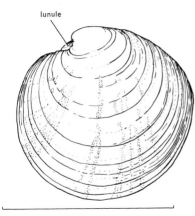

lunule

Dosinia exoleta

Dosinia lupinus

Lucinoma borealis

Diplodonta rotundata

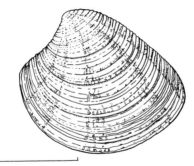

Venus striatula

Venus fasciata (da Costa)

Length: 20 mm; *Height:* 18 mm.

Diagnostic characters: Resembles *V. striatula* generally but has broader ribs set further apart; ligament cannot be seen from outside when valves closed; variably coloured, often with darker streaks or rays.

Habitat: In sand or coarser gravel, from lower shore and deeper water; widely distributed.

Venus casina (L.)

Length: 45 mm; *Height:* 42 mm.

Diagnostic characters: Shell usually off-white, but may have reddish-brown rays; distinguished by prominent raised, sharp-edged concentric ridges, otherwise shows typical features of venus shell.

Habitat: An off-shore species, widely distributed and quite frequently found, burrowing in sand or sandy gravel.

General features: This represents one of several venus shells more typically found in deeper waters, but which might be found washed up on the beach. Others include the strong *V. verrucosa* L. (55 mm), with a rough, knobbly-surfaced shell, the large (75 mm) *Callista chione* (L.), with a thick, glossy-smooth, rather oval shell, and the much smaller (15 mm) *Venus ovata* Pennant, characterised by the shell surface bearing 40–50 diverging ribs, giving it a cockle-like appearance.

Mercenaria mercenaria (L.)

Length: 75 mm (can grow larger); *Height:* 70 mm.

Diagnostic characters: Shell large, well-built; concentrically ridged, with occasional fine radiating lines; light greyish-brown, but sometimes with darker zig-zag markings; structurally like other venus shells but with distinctive roughened area on hinge beneath ligament.

Habitat: In muddy gravel, mostly off-shore in shallow water; an introduced species but now established off parts of the south coast.

General features: Mercenaria, the Quahog or hard shell clam, introduced from North America, where it is a recognised delicacy, and first established here temporarily in the Humber during the last century, has since become established in quite large colonies in the Solent, Southampton Water and Portsmouth Harbour. These have probably been derived from specimens brought in by transatlantic ships. The success of attempts to cultivate the American clam on a larger scale in British waters suggests that it might become an increasingly important item of food in this country.

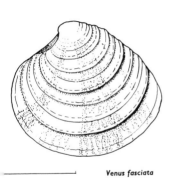

Venus fasciata

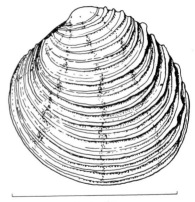

Venus casina

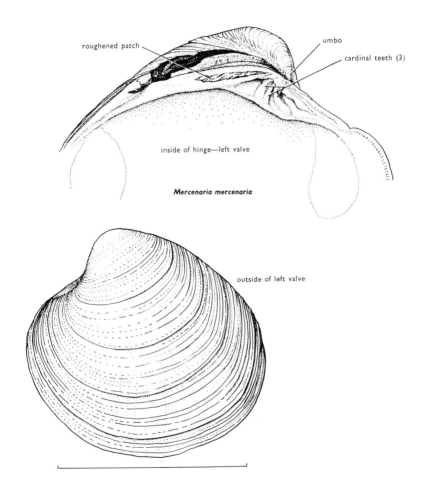

roughened patch

umbo

cardinal teeth (3)

inside of hinge—left valve

Mercenaria mercenaria

outside of left valve

Venerupis rhomboides (Pennant)

Length: 50 mm; *Height:* 32 mm.

Diagnostic characters: Shell strong, largely oval, umbones in anterior half and turned forwards; surface with numerous concentric ridges but lacking radial lines; valve margin smooth; rather glossy surface, pale with reddish-brown or purple zig-zag or irregular markings; pallial sinus not reaching midpoint of shell.

Habitat: Low-water mark and below, in coarse sand or gravel; widely distributed.

General features: This is one of five British species of *Venerupis* (the carpet shells), often distinctively patterned, and distinguished from other venerids by their oblong shape and the umbones being much nearer the anterior end. Individual species are not easy to separate and one needs to look at internal features, e.g. nature of the pallial sinus, as well as external shell characteristics. The smooth-shelled *V. rhomboides* is one of the largest and commonest species, although more frequent off-shore. Also in deeper water is *V. aurea* (Gmelin), with a smaller, still smooth shell, but bearing fine radial lines as well as concentric ridges.

Venerupis pullastra (Montagu)

Length: 42 mm; *Height:* 30 mm.

Diagnostic characters: Shell broadly oval and similar in general form to *V. rhomboides* but with sharper curve on upper edge posteriorly; surface not glossy with concentric ridges crossed by fine radiating ribs; yellowish-white with variegated darker brown or purplish markings; pallial sinus deep, extending further than midpoint of shell (see also fig. 10); byssus.

Habitat: In gravelly sand, below rocks or in empty shells, usually attached by byssus; lower shore downwards; widely distributed.

Venerupis decussata (L.)

Length: 54 mm; *Height:* 40 mm.

Diagnostic characters: Shell heavy, generally similar to *V. pullastra* but more squared off posteriorly and more prominently sculptured; marked radial ribs intersect concentric ridges to produce criss-cross or decussate effect; off-white with darker brown or purplish markings but less brightly coloured than *V. pullastra*; pallial sinus does not reach centre of shell, and region below it is clearly wedge-shaped.

Habitat: On lower shore, as well as off-shore, in muddy sand or sandy gravel; mainly off south and west coasts.

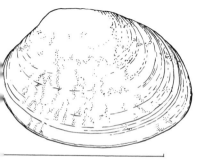

Venerupis rhomboides

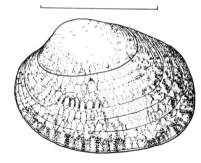

Venerupis pullastra

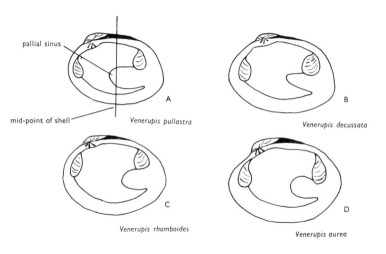

pallial sinus

mid-point of shell

Venerupis pullastra A

Venerupis decussata B

Venerupis rhomboides C

Venerupis aurea D

Venerupis shells—inside of right valves showing pallial sinus (A, B, C x $\frac{1}{2}$; D x $\frac{3}{4}$)
(after Holme)

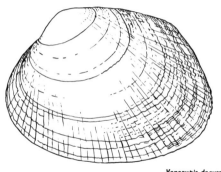

Venerupis decussata

Venerupis saxatilis (Fleuriau)

Length: 20 mm; *Height:* 14 mm.

Diagnostic characters: Shell smaller than other venerupids, often irregular and distorted due to habitat (see below); prominent concentric ridges raised and folded posteriorly; byssus.

Habitat: In rock crevices and in holes vacated by rock-borers, attached by the byssus; intertidal, mainly on southern coasts.

Donax vittatus (da Costa)

Length: 26 mm; *Height:* 14 mm.

Diagnostic characters: Shell strong, wedge-shaped, inequilateral, with anterior half larger; umbones in posterior half pointed medially and posteriorly; surface glossy with fine radiating lines; variably and brightly coloured, inner surface white or coloured with purple or violet blotches; internal margin of valves ridged.

Habitat: In firm sand in large, open, i.e. exposed bays; lower shore and below; widely distributed.

General features: Donax represents the so-called wedge shells, characterised by their shape and beautiful, highly glossed surface. *D. variegatus* (Gmelin) is even shinier than *D. vittatus* and is distinguished by an almost smooth margin; it is restricted to the south-west.

Gari depressa (Pennant)

Length: 35 mm; *Height;* 19 mm.

Diagnostic characters: Shell solid, nearly equilateral, oval appearance, margins gape posteriorly; pale, yellowish-white, often with purple or pinkish radiating rays (hence the popular name 'sunset shell'); inside of shell polished, may be purple or variably coloured; valve margin smooth.

Habitat: In sand, mainly off-shore, but very occasionally at low water; widely distributed, but more likely to be found in the south and west.

Gari fervensis (Gmelin)

Length: 44 mm; *Height:* 22 mm.

Diagnostic characters: Shell more oblong than *G. depressa* with upper edge abruptly angled posteriorly; keel in posterior half; surface with concentric ridges; slight gape at rear; pale pink or occasionally darker, with radiating cream or yellowish rays; polished inner surface, sometimes purple-tinged.

Habitat: Low-water mark or off-shore, in sand; widely distributed.

Venerupis saxatilis

Donax vittatus

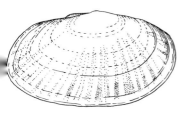

Gari depressa

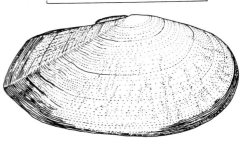

Gari fervensis

Tellina tenuis da Costa

Length: 22 mm; *Height:* 15 mm.

Diagnostic characters: Shell flattened, thin and brittle, generally oval; glossy surface, white, yellow, orange, rose or pink; prominent external ligament; very deep pallial sinus; siphons very long.

Habitat: Buried in clean sand from mid-tide down to shallow water offshore; widely distributed, common.

General features: This species introduces the Tellinidae, a family of thin, flattened bivalves adapted to burrow deeply into mud or sand. They have extremely long delicate separate siphons, of which the inhalant draws in particulate organic matter deposited on the surface of the substrate, i.e. they are deposit feeders. *T. tenuis* is one of the most common of this type of bivalve, forming dense populations, up to 10 cm or so beneath the surface, down towards low water. The delicately coloured shells are often seen lying empty on the surface of the sand, and if intact opened out like butterfly-wings by the elasticity of the ligament. The related *T. fabula* Gmelin is smaller, more twisted posteriorly, with the right valve bearing characteristic oblique striations; it is found at low-water mark and below.

Tellina crassa Pennant

Length: 50 mm; *Height:* 42 mm.

Diagnostic characters: Shell solid and well built, whitish, with many well marked concentric ridges; rounded oval with characteristic twist on lower margin posteriorly (this flexure of the rear part of the shell is found in many tellinids but is particularly noticeable here); deep pallial sinus protrudes upwards across inner surface of shell.

Habitat: Mainly off-shore species in sand or coarser substrate; fairly generally distributed but more often off southern and western coasts.

Macoma balthica (L.)

Length: 14 mm (may be larger); *Height:* 11 mm.

Diagnostic characters: Shell stronger than *T. tenuis*, rounder and more swollen; surface with fine concentric striations; colour variable; prominent external ligament.

Habitat: Tends to favour muddier substrate than *T. tenuis*; lives in muddy sand or gravel, between tidemarks down to low water, often in estuaries (*Macoma* tolerates low substrates and is found in the Baltic, hence its specific name); widely distributed, common.

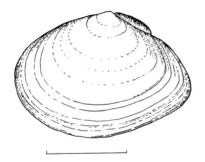

Tellina tenuis

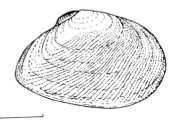

Tellina fabula

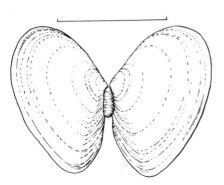

Tellina tenuis—valves opened out

½ nat. size

Tellina crassa

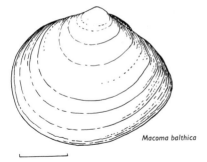

Macoma balthica

Scrobicularia plana (da Costa)

Length: 45 mm; *Height:* 36 mm.

Diagnostic characters: Shell stronger than in *Tellina tenuis* or *Macoma*, largely oval, opaque; surface sculpture of ridges and lines; usually light brownish-yellow; ligament less marked externally and there is a prominent internal ligament.

Habitat: In mud or muddy sand, intertidal or in estuaries but higher up than *Macoma*; widely distributed.

General features: This species favours a very soft, muddy substrate, with high organic content, and is the largest deposit feeder of the bivalves described. It has extremely long extensible siphons which enable it to live buried down to 25 cm beneath the surface.

Abra alba (Wood)

Length: 22 mm; *Height:* 15 mm.

Diagnostic characters: Shell much smaller and more delicate than *Scrobicularia*; generally oval in shape and very white and shiny, with umbones in posterior half.

Habitat: In muddy ground, mainly off-shore, and widely distributed; can be common on suitable ground.

General features: This is one representative of four species of *Alba*, all with flat, thin whitish shells, which may be numerous in muddy substrates of estuaries and deeper waters, feeding, like *Scrobicularia*, on the rich bottom deposits.

Pharus legumen (L.)

Length: 86 mm; *Height:* 18 mm.

Diagnostic characters: Shell brittle, elongate and pod-shaped, gaping; nearly equilateral, with ligament external and prominent, almost in the mid-line on the upper surface; yellowish, glossy surface; siphons rather long and separate.

Habitat: In sand at extreme low water; whole specimens not easy to find but empty shells not uncommon in sandy bays; most often found on south and west coasts, off Wales and Ireland, except the north.

General features: This shell resembles in shape the Solenidae (razor-shells) described below but is in fact a closer relative of the tellins. It can easily be distinguished by the position of the ligament, which is centrally placed on the upper surface in *Pharus*, but at the anterior end in the true razor-shells. When empty, the shell of *Pharus* springs open due to the opening thrust of the elastic ligament, as does the shell of other tellins in similar circumstances.

Scrobicularia plana

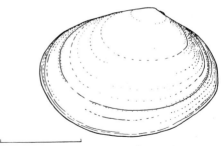

Abra alba

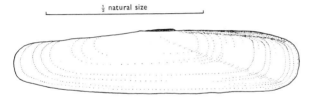

½ natural size

Pharus legumen

Ensis siliqua (L.)

Length: 200 mm; *Height:* 30 mm.

Diagnostic characters: Shell long and narrow, almost straight; rectangular, gaping at both ends, which are abruptly squared off;
umbones and ligament at anterior end; yellowish-green streaked with
brown; foot creamy-white; siphons short, separated only at tip.

Habitat: In clean sand, low water downwards; widely distributed.

General features: This and the following few species represent the
Solenidae, the aptly named razor-shells. They are beautifully designed
for rapid vertical burrowing through sand with their unmistakable
elongated shell and the large powerful foot. The rapidity of movement
is well known to the would-be collector trying to dig out an intact
specimen at low water, where the lunging fork is more likely to miss
the razor-shell completely or bring up only a portion of its body. The
bivalve is equally adept at returning vertically to the surface when the
danger of attack or of exposure disappears. The razor-shells, sometimes known as razorfish or spoutfish, are edible and regarded as
local delicacies in Orkney and Northern Ireland. In addition to the
species of *Ensis* described here, mention might be made also of
Solen marginatus Montagu (115 mm), found locally off south and
west coasts and distinguishable by a deep groove behind and parallel
to the front edge of the shell, and the small (25 mm), delicate,
Cultellus [*Phaxas*] *pellucidus* (Pennant), widely distributed and quite
frequent in deeper water, characterised by a pale, translucent shell
with a distinctly curved lower edge.

Ensis arcuatus (Jeffreys)

Length: 150 mm; *Height:* 20 mm.

Diagnostic characters: Shell shorter and slightly curved, compared with
E. siliqua, especially along lower edge; posterior end tapers a little,
anterior edge squared off; foot creamy-white.

Habitat: Widely distributed in sand or coarser substrate, extreme low
water and off-shore.

Ensis ensis (L.)

Length: 100 mm; *Height:* 13 mm.

Diagnostic characters: Shell shorter and more curved still than *E.
arcuatus*, the curvature affecting both upper and lower margins;
anterior edge roundish, posterior end tapers notably; foot pale
red-brown.

Habitat: As for *E. arcuatus* but in relatively fine sand.

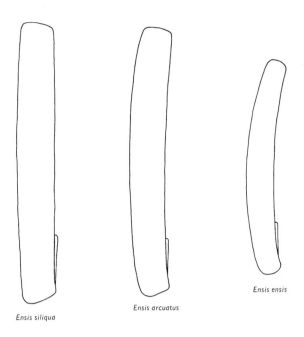

Ensis siliqua

Ensis arcuatus

Ensis ensis

(after Holme with some modification of *E. arcuatus*)

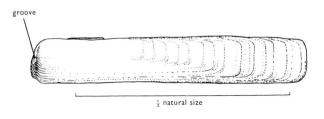

groove

½ natural size

Solen marginatus

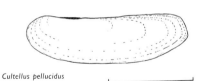

Cultellus pellucidus

Mactra corallina (L.)

Length: 48 mm; *Height:* 36 mm.

Diagnostic characters: Shell brittle, equilateral, with umbones centrally placed, gaping slightly posteriorly; mainly triangular; creamy or yellowish-white with brown rays radiating from the umbones; lateral hinge teeth smooth; two cardinal (central) hinge teeth in the left valve unite to form a characteristic ∧ shape.

Habitat: In clean sand at low-water mark and off-shore; both whole animals and empty shells may be washed up at low water spring tides on open sandy shores; widely distributed.

General features: This attractive bivalve introduces the Mactridae (trough shells), with their symmetrical rather triangular-shaped valves. They have relatively short siphons and are shallow but efficient burrowers using an effective rocking movement of the shell to dig their way down into the sand. Most are off-shore species and they make up an important section of the bottom fauna (benthos) on the seabed.

Spisula solida (L.)

Length: 45 mm; *Height:* 35 mm.

Diagnostic characters: Shell thicker and more solid than *Mactra*, broadly triangular but with rounded edges; surface with concentric lines, off-white; two cardinal teeth in left valve have ∧-shaped appearance; lateral hinge teeth finely serrated; fan-shaped pattern of grooves on upper (dorsal) area.

Habitat: In sandy substrates, extreme low-water mark but mainly off-shore; widely distributed.

General features: This is one of the best known of the *Spisula* shells, generally distinguished from *Mactra* by their rather stronger nature, and the delicately grooved lateral hinge teeth. The other two species of *Spisula*, both frequent and living in similar habitats, are not easy to separate. *S. subtruncata* (da Costa) (26 mm), is usually smaller than *S. solida*, with prominent umbones and a more angular shape, especially posteriorly, and two particularly well-marked areas of fan-shaped grooves adjoining the umbones. *S. elliptica* (Brown) (30 mm), is more elliptical in shape, thinner-shelled, and has smooth, not grooved, upper (dorsal) areas.

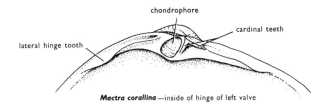

Mactra corallina—inside of hinge of left valve

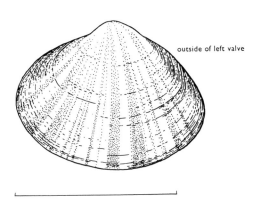

outside of left valve

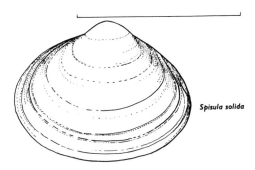

Spisula solida

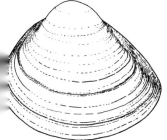

Spisula subtruncata

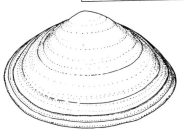

Spisula elliptica

Lutraria lutraria (L.)

Length: 112 mm; *Height:* 65 mm.

Diagnostic characters: Shell heavy, largely elliptical; equivalve, gaping at either end; olive-brown periostracum covers yellowish-white shell; in both valves the ligament is attached to a triangular-shaped pit (chondrophore); deep pallial sinus; siphons long, fused together and covered by horny sheath with purple-brown markings.

Habitat: Burrows deeply in mud or muddy sand, low-water mark and off-shore; widely distributed.

General features: This is the commonest species of *Lutraria* (the otter shell), which, like the Myidae (gapers) described below, lives buried deeply in a soft substrate using the large, fused siphons to maintain contact with the water above. The more elongated *L. magna* (da Costa) is locally distributed off southern and western coasts, whilst the thicker-shelled *L. angustior* Philippi occurs locally off the south coast; both can be distinguished from *L. lutraria* by the shape and position of the pallial sinus.

Mya arenaria L.

Length: 105 mm; *Height:* 65 mm.

Diagnostic characters: Shell solid, broadly oval, inequivalve, gaping at posterior end; surface with concentric ridges and clear growth stages, with a few ill-defined markings; greyish-white or dull brown; left valve only with large protruding spoon-shaped projection (chondrophore) for internal ligament; deep pallial sinus; siphons long, fused and covered by a periostracal sheath.

Habitat: In firm mud, muddy sand or sand; lower shore and often in estuaries; widely distributed.

General features: *Mya*, the so-called sand gaper, or edible soft-shelled clam is a deep but not active burrower, a feature of the Myidae and their relatives. The long, very substantial siphons emerging from the widely gaping shell extend to the surface or withdraw as required, the animal itself remaining relatively stationary.

Mya truncata L.

Length: 50 mm; *Height:* 34 mm.

Diagnostic characters: Shell well-built, posterior end markedly blunt or truncated, and gaping widely; inequivalve; greyish-white; other features as for *M. arenaria*.

Habitat: In sand, muddy gravel, or clay, lower shore and below; generally distributed.

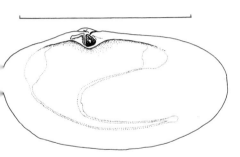

L. angustior (after Holme)

L. magna (after Holme)

Lutraria lutraria—inside of right valve

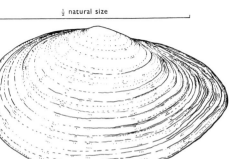

½ natural size

Mya arenaria—outisde of left valve

protruding chondrophore

deep pallial sinus

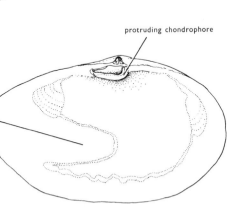

Mya arenaria—inside of left valve

Mya truncata—left valve

Corbula gibba (Olivi)

Length: 13 mm; *Height:* 10 mm.

Diagnostic characters: Shell small and markedly inequivalve, the right valve being much the larger and swelling over the left; the horny edge of the latter fits perfectly inside the rim of the larger valve; greyish-brown; internal ligament attached to a chondrophore (as in the gapers).

Habitat: Frequent all around the British Isles on muddy sand or gravel; mainly off-shore but may be found at extreme low water.

Hiatella arctica (L.)

Length: 35 mm; *Height:* 18 mm.

Diagnostic characters: Shell solid, broadly rectangular but variable in shape; gapes posteriorly; ridged surface, white; external ligament; extensible siphons, red-tipped, with horny sheath; byssus.

Habitat: Nestles within crevices or *Laminaria* holdfasts attached by byssus, or burrows mechanically into soft rock, including limestone or sandstone (best shown by breaking open rock where holes can be seen through which the 'red noses' of the siphons are visible); lower shore downwards; widely distributed, common.

Pholas dactylus L.   Common piddock

Length: 100 mm; *Height:* 35 mm.

Diagnostic characters: Shell brittle, elongate, indented and gaping at the front; 40–50 rows of spines on the surface produced where radiating ribs cross concentric ridges; white; four accessory plates; process (apophysis) on inner surface attached to hinge region (characteristic of pholads—see fig. of *Zirfaea* facing p. 190); ligament small, often difficult to define; no byssus.

Habitat: Burrows into shale, slate, chalk, red sandstone, wood and peat; lower shore to shallow water; south and south-west coasts; S. Wales.

General features: This and the immediately following group of species constitute the Pholadidae (the so-called piddocks), one of the best known and most highly adapted of bivalves specialised for boring into a wide variety of substrates. Burrowing is effected purely mechanically by means of the spiny anterior surface of the hard but brittle shell. The process is facilitated by a rocking movement of the valves made possible by the almost complete absence of the ligament.

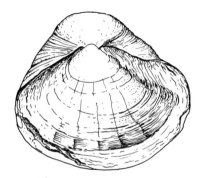

Corbula gibba

Hiatella arctica

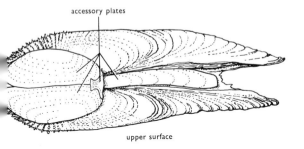

accessory plates

upper surface

Pholas dactylus

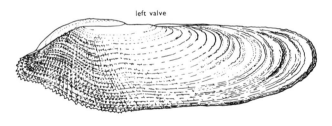

left valve

Zirfaea crispata (L.)

Length: 50 mm; *Height:* 30 mm.

Diagnostic characters: Shell substantial, broadly oval, gaping at both ends; groove divides each valve into anterior and posterior regions, with 20 or so rows of prickly spines on the former; white; strong, prominent apophysis; single small accessory plate.

Habitat: Bores into peat, clay, shale, sandstone or oolite, not usually wood; low-water mark and off-shore; widely distributed.

Barnea candida (L.)

Length: 52 mm; *Height:* 17 mm.

Diagnostic characters: Shell brittle, generally oval and thin, swollen; chalky-white; surface with rows of small prickly spines formed where concentric ridges cross radiating ribs, most pronounced anteriorly; one upper (dorsal) accessory plate.

Habitat: Bores into a wide range of substrates, including peat, wood, sand and various soft rocks, producing mainly horizontal burrows; lower shore and off-shore; widely distributed.

General features: There are several other well-known piddocks, although often with a rather limited distribution. *B. parva* (Pennant) (45 mm long) has a more solid shell, white in colour although often stained reddish-brown by the substrate, e.g. red sandstone, through which it bores. This species is limited to south-western and southern coasts around to Kent (Whitstable). Restricted to the south-west also is the unusual *Pholadidea loscombiana* Turton, with a paper-thin, brittle shell, bearing a cup-like horny extension posteriorly protecting the base of the siphons. Not all clay- or rock-boring bivalves are members of the Pholadidae. The so-called American piddock, *Petricola pholadiformis* Lamarck (shell 46 mm long), is in fact a member of the Veneridae (see p. 170). Although its elongate shell, with prominent ridges and spines externally, superficially resembles that of a pholad, the presence of hinge teeth and the lack of apophyses and accessory plates clearly distinguishes it from the shell of a true piddock. The similarity is an instance of parallel evolution. *Petricola* is an imported species, which has become established at a number of localities, e.g. Whitstable, where it is the dominant borer in stiff clay on the lower shore.

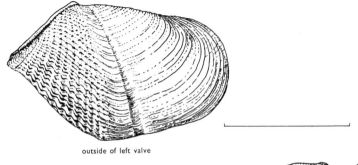

outside of left valve

Zirfaea crispata

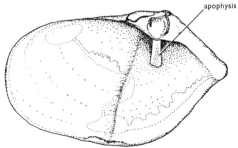

apophysis

inside of left valve

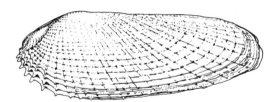

Barnea candida

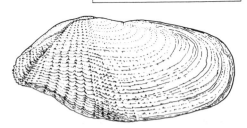

Petricola pholadiformis

Barnea parva

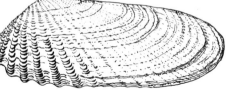

Nototeredo [*Teredo*] *norvagicus* (Spengler)

Shelly tube containing animal: Length: 300 mm; *Height:* 16 mm.
Shell: Length: 16 mm; *Height:* 16 mm.

Diagnostic characters: Shell very reduced, brittle, helmet-shaped, into which animal cannot withdraw; animal long, worm-like, in long shelly tube; siphons very long, fused except at tips, where two paddle-shaped calcareous 'pallets' close the opening of the burrow.

Habitat: Bores in wood in seawater, either submerged (e.g. pier piles, groynes) or floating (boats, drift-wood, etc.); widely distributed.

General features: This is the largest representative of *Teredo* and its relatives, the so-called shipworms, remarkable and specialised wood-borers, related to the piddocks, which use the modified shell as an efficient cutting surface. As the animal burrows, it grows in length but maintains contact with the exterior through the elongated siphons. When these are withdrawn, the opening is effectively sealed by a pair of limy plates or pallets enabling the bivalve to survive for days or weeks without contact with seawater. The wood particles and shavings produced by boring form the major source of food, part of the alimentary canal being specialised for its digestion. The burrows, lined by a protective limy coating, may completely riddle badly infected timber and cause serious damage to pier supports. Their popular name derives from the association *Teredo* inevitably had with ships in the days of wood and sail, when infection with the shipworm was often disastrous to the timbers. Related species are distinguished from each other by the form of the shell and especially the pallets. In the much smaller, but also common, *Teredo navalis* L., the pallets are deeply indented at the tip.

Xylophaga dorsalis Turton

Shell: Length: 10 mm; *Height:* 9 mm.

Diagnostic characters: Shell delicate, rather globular and helmet-shaped, divided into anterior and posterior regions by a double ridge and groove; dorsal accessory places (mesoplax) in two halves; shell encloses body completely, only siphons project; no pallets.

Habitat: Bores into submerged wood; widely distributed.

General features: This species is a less advanced wood borer than the shipworms, and more closely related to the pholads previously described. *Xylophaga* uses its burrow for protection like other piddocks and relies on particles suspended in the water for food; it cannot digest wood like *Teredo* and its relatives.

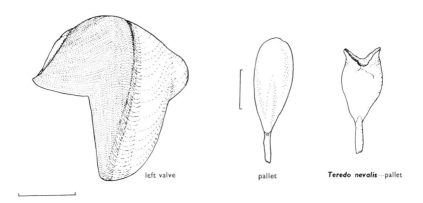

left valve

pallet

Teredo nevalis—pallet

Nototeredo norvagicus

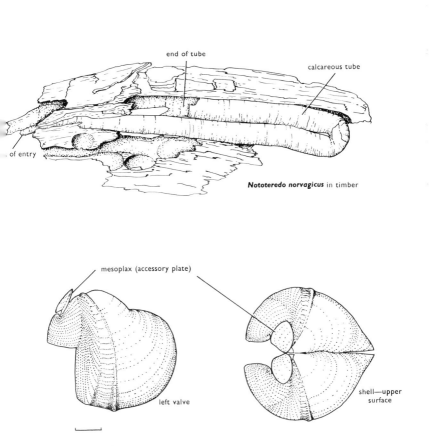

end of tube

calcareous tube

of entry

Nototeredo norvagicus in timber

mesoplax (accessory plate)

left valve

shell—upper surface

Xylophaga dorsalis

Other marine bivalvia

Brief mention might be made here of representatives of certain rather specialised groups found more typically in deeper waters. Species of *Thracia*, some individuals found at extreme low water but more usually off-shore, are generally characterised by a very fragile, whitish shell. *Cuspidaria cuspidata* (Olivi), in which the shell (18 mm long) is distinguished by an unmistakable posterior spout-like process, represents an unusual group of deep-water, carnivorous bivalves, the Septibranchia. In these forms the gills are modified as muscular, pumping sheets, whereby the prey, usually dead and decaying crustaceans, are drawn towards the mouth.

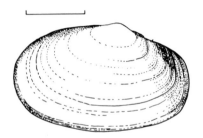

Thracia villosiuscula

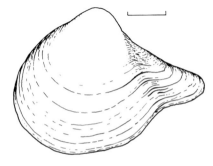

Cuspidaria cuspidata

Key to Freshwater Bivalvia

1. Shell pointed anteriorly, triangular in end-view; characteristic zig-zag markings; attached to substrate by threads (byssus) . .
   Dreissena polymorpha (p. 202)
   Shell oval or rounded, smooth curved outline in end-view; not attached to substrate; usually burrowing forms 2

2. Shell commonly over 25 mm long, oval or elongate; edges of mantle free (Unionacea) 3
   Shell less than 25 mm long, rounded; edges of mantle partly fused (Sphaeriacea) 7

3. Hinge lacking teeth; shell with raised wing-like processes along upper margin posteriorly 4
   Hinge bears teeth; shell without wing-like processes postero-dorsally 5

4. Shell rather flat; very large, up to 140 mm or more long; upper edge straight; greenish-yellow colour; posterior foot retractor and shell adductor muscle scars separate . . . .
   Anodonta cygnea (p. 198)
   Shell obviously swollen; smaller, 90 mm long; upper edge markedly raised posteriorly; rather thicker and darker shell; posterior foot retractor and shell adductor muscle scars combined . . . . *Anodonta anatina* (p. 198)

5. Umbones lowered and usually worn away . . . . . .
   Margaritifera margaritifera (p. 196)
   Umbones swollen and raised 6

6. Shell elongate, thinner posteriorly . . *Unio pictorum* (p. 196)
   Shell more oval, swollen prominently especially at anterior end . . . . *Unio tumidus* (p. 196)

7. Rounded shells with umbones slightly anterior to the mid-line; usually over 10 mm long; double siphons . . . .
   Sphaerium spp. (p. 200)
   Less symmetrical shells with umbones behind mid-line; commonly less than 10 mm long; single siphon . . . .
   Pisidium spp. (p. 200)

Margaritifera margaritifera (L.)

Length: 100 mm; *Height:* 50 mm.

Diagnostic characters: Shell thick, elongate; umbones low and usually eroded unevenly giving appearance of corrosion; brown to black; inner surface nacreous (mother-of-pearl); hinge teeth.

Habitat: Usually, although not always, in soft water; favours sand-based fast-moving rivers; England and Wales in an area north and west of the line from Beer Head to Scarborough; Scotland, except eastern lowlands; Ireland, except central area.

General features: This and the next group of species constitute the Unionacea, large freshwater mussels which are structurally more advanced than their marine name-sakes, and, unlike them, essentially burrowers in soft muddy or sandy substrates. *Margaritifera*, the so-called pearl mussel, may produce quite sizeable pearls, which are secreted by the mantle and consist of concentric layers of nacre, the same material that constitutes the inner, iridescent layer of the shell. The claimed separate species, *M. durrovensis* Phillips, found in the River Nore in Ireland, is now generally considered to be a hard-water variety of the type species, which itself normally frequents soft waters.

Unio pictorum (L.)

Length: 90 mm; *Height:* 40 mm.

Diagnostic characters: Shell solid, rounded, quite swollen at front end (but not as much as *U. tumidus* described below), elongate and thinning posteriorly, although very variable in shape; brown or yellow-green; nearly straight lower margin; hinge teeth.

Habitat: Hard water, in canals, rivers, lakes, reservoirs and large ponds; England and Wales, like a number of other freshwater species, in the region bounding the canal system, but not Scotland and Ireland.

Unio tumidus Philipsson

Length: 80 mm; *Height:* 40 mm.

Diagnostic characters: Shell thick, oval, very tumid anteriorly; posterior region shorter than in *U. pictorum*; dark brown or greenish, sometimes with radiating yellow rays; umbones prominent, expanded and elevated; lower margin gently curved; hinge teeth.

Habitat: Also hard water, in canals and slow-running rivers; England, Somerset to Yorkshire; Wales, not Scotland and Ireland; less frequent than *U. pictorum* and showing less variable shell form.

Margaritifera margaritifera

Unio pictorum

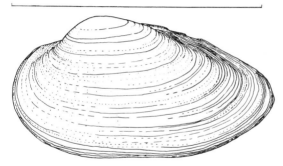

Unio tumidus

Anodonta cygnea (L.)

Length: Up to 140 mm; *Height:* 68 mm.

Diagnostic characters: Shell large, rather thin but of uniform thickness; not usually swollen; upper margin mainly straight and generally parallel to mid-lower region; surface glossy but with concentric ridges; yellowish to yellow-green; separate posterior foot retractor and adductor muscle scars; no hinge teeth.

Habitat: In hard water; favours muddy bottom of slow-moving rivers, canals, lakes, reservoirs and large ponds; found in most of England and Ireland, parts of Wales, and southernmost Scotland.

General features: This species, the so-called swan mussel, is perhaps the best known of the larger unionid mussels, which possess stoutly developed gills. In the female these house the young larval stages, known as glochidia, which are ultimately discharged with the outgoing (exhalant) water current. They do not develop further unless they come into contact with a fish, for example, the three-spined stickleback, when they embed themselves in the skin, usually in the fins or tail region. Here they embark on a truly parasitic period of existence. Finally to complete this unique life history, they break free as incipient adults and develop to maturity on the bottom.

Anodonta anatina (L.)

Length: 90 mm; *Height:* 55 mm.

Diagnostic characters: Shell smaller than *A. cygnea*, thicker, especially anteriorly, and swollen, although variable in form; well developed elongated wing-like processes behind the umbones making dorsal and ventral borders diverge appreciably at posterior end; lower margin more curved; surface with finer ridges; colour darker than *A. cygnea*, greenish-brown; posterior foot retractor and adductor muscle scars combined; no hinge teeth.

Habitat: In hard water, favouring flowing waters with a sandy rather than a muddy bed, but also in canals and large ponds; distribution as for *A. cygnea* but more widespread in Scotland and restricted locally to central Ireland. Less common than both these species and locally distributed in rivers, and occasionally canals, from southern counties of England north to Yorkshire, is *A. complanata* Rossmassler. Its shell is flattened like that of *A. cygnea* but with more divergent posterior margins. More specifically diagnostic are distinctive, tubercle-like undulating ridges (rugae) near the umbones, not found in the other species.

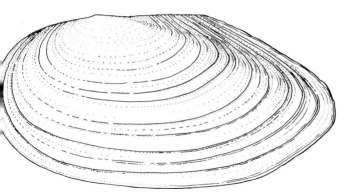

Anodonta cygnea

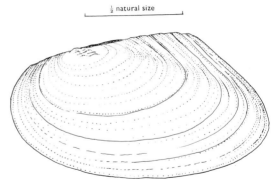

Anodonta complanata

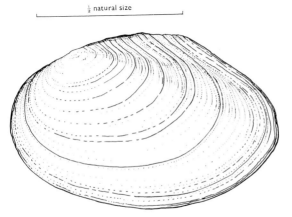

Anodonta anatina

Sphaerium corneum (L.)

Length: 11 mm; *Height:* 9 mm.

Diagnostic characters: Shell small, thin-walled, rounded and swollen; nearly equilateral, but with the umbones slightly anterior to the mid-line; pale yellowish-brown; hinge teeth; 2 long siphons.

Habitat: Widely distributed in most freshwater habitats, but favouring moving water in rivers, canals and large ditches.

General features: This is the commonest species of *Sphaerium*, the small but ubiquitous orb-shell mussels, which, with *Pisidium* below, comprise the Sphaeriacea. Unlike the larger unionid mussels they are hermaphrodite and the young, although they attach themselves by a byssus, do not pass through a parasitic phase. *S. corneum* commonly lives on the bottom in mud, but it may also be found on the stems of water plants. More locally distributed in canals and larger rivers is *S. rivicola*, which is the largest species, reaching 24 mm in length. Half this size is the fragile *S. lacustre* (Müller), distinguished by its cone-shaped umbones, which frequents ponds and ditches and tolerates more adverse conditions than the other species.

Pisidium amnicum (Müller)

Length: 9 mm; *Height:* 7 mm.

Diagnostic characters: Shell small, broader hinge and more swollen than *Sphaerium;* inequilateral, umbones posterior to mid-line; yellowish to brown; well-developed hinge teeth; one short fused siphon.

Habitat: In hard, clear water, preferably flowing; fairly generally distributed.

General features: This is the largest of 16 species of *Pisidium*, tiny bivalves (the so-called pea mussels), which are difficult to separate and identify (for detailed analysis see comprehensive synopsis by Ellis referred to in Appendix). *Pisidium* species are widespread in many freshwater habitats, their dispersal probably being facilitated by their small size. Some are almost ubiquitous, e.g. *P. casertanum* Poli, and *P. subtruncatum* Malm; others, unlike *P. amnicum* and typical hard-water species, favour soft waters, for example, *P. nitidum* Jenyns. A few, e.g., *P. personatum* Malm, often with a red-encrusted shell, favours 'bad' localities, e.g. shallow ditches and temporary ponds, avoided by many other species.

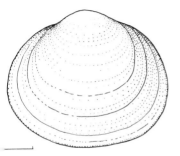

Sphaerium corneum

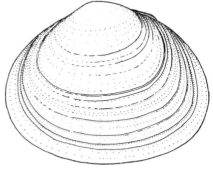

Sphaerium rivicola

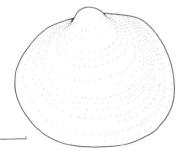

Sphaerium lacustre

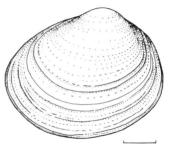

Pisidium amnicum

Dreissena polymorpha (Pallas)

Length: 30 mm; *Height:* 15 mm.

Diagnostic characters: Shell thickish and swollen, with umbones at pointed anterior end; bears strong keel and appears triangular in end-view; zig-zag markings on yellowish-brown background; attached by byssus.

Habitat: In canals, slow-moving rivers, docks, reservoirs and water mains, attached often in clusters to hard surfaces, including stones, rocks and wooden uprights, by byssus threads; generally distributed in England and also in central Scotland.

General features: This rather striking bivalve, the so-called 'Zebra mussel' because of its stripy appearance, resembles the marine mussel, *Mytilus*, more closely both in form and habit (e.g. by byssal attachment) than other freshwater lamellibranchs. Its links with marine forms are also illustrated by its possession of a free-living ciliated larval stage known as the veliger, which after a period swimming free in the water sinks to the bottom and metamorphoses into the adult, without recourse to a parasitic stage like that found in the freshwater unionid bivalves. The potential dangers of these larvae being swept away by currents has probably restricted *Dreissena* to a habitat of slow-moving or static waters. It was found in Britain originally in 1824, probably brought in with ships from the Baltic, and subsequently spread rapidly through the canal system by 1840. This network of waterways, completed in the first part of the nineteenth century, has provided a suitable natural habitat for many freshwater molluscs, and has facilitated their spread throughout the 'canal basin' of England and Wales.

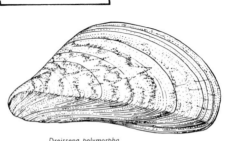

Dreissena polymorpha

CLASS: CEPHALOPODA

The cephalopods, exemplified by the squids, cuttlefish, and octopods, represent the peak of molluscan evolution. They are active and predatory animals, and as recent work on their brain and neurosensory system demonstrates, show a high degree of intelligence. Except in the primitive *Nautilus*, found in tropical waters, which retains an external shell, large and many-chambered, the shell in most cephalopods is internal, reduced or almost absent.

The now muscular mantle is the motive force in movement which is predominantly a jet propulsive mechanism best developed in the squids and cuttlefish. In this, water is forced out of the mantle cavity via a funnel or siphon which acts as the jet, the efficiency and power of the system increasing with age and size. The suckered arms or tentacles, ten in number in the Decapoda (squid and cuttlefish) and eight in the Octopoda (e.g. *Octopus*), are used to capture the prey, which is then broken up by the powerful jaws assisted by the radula. These beak-like jaws may be used in identification; in some large deep-sea squids found in the stomach of their predators, the sperm whales, the beaks are practically the only known parts of the mollusc. Cephalopods show remarkable ability to change colour, especially when disturbed, and as a protective measure they can also disgorge a black, inky fluid.

Decapoda

Ten tentacles or arms, two longer than the others.

Sepia officinalis L.   Common cuttlefish
Length: 300 mm.

Diagnostic characters: Body broad with lateral elongated fins (the related *S. elegans* Orbigny is smaller and narrower); internal shell constitutes 'cuttlebone'; back often exhibits stripy pattern but showing variable colour changes when alive.

Habitat: May come fairly near the shore amongst eel-grass; widely distributed but more frequent in south.

Sepiola atlantica Orbigny
Length: 35 mm.

Diagnostic characters: Small with roundish body and lateral fins lobe-like; mantle fused to upper surface of head.

Habitat: Widely distributed and quite frequently found partly buried in sand in very shallow water at low tide, especially in summer; can be caught with shrimping nets, or with shrimp trawls in deeper water. The similarly shaped but larger *Rossia macrosoma* (Chiaje) is found only off Scottish coasts; unlike *Sepiola* the mantle edge is free and not attached to the head region.

Loligo forbesii Steenstrup   Common squid
Length: 300 mm.

Diagnostic characters: Slim, elongated body with lateral fins triangularly-shaped; shell an internal horny 'pen'.

Habitat: This active swimmer is rarely seen inshore but it can be trawled, especially in the spring; widely distributed.

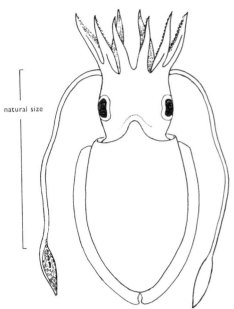

natural size

Sepia officinalis
dorsal view

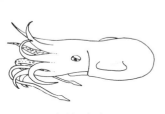

Sepiola atlantica

$\frac{1}{4}$
natural
size

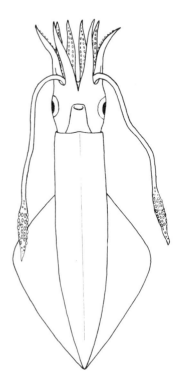

Loligo forbesii

Octopoda

Eight similar tentacles or arms.

Octopus vulgaris Lamarck

Length: 450 mm.

Diagnostic characters: Body sac-like; tentacles bear two rows of suckers.

Habitat: At low water, in pools or hidden in crevices, on southern coasts; slow-moving, crawls rather than swims.

Eledone cirrhosa (Lamarck)

Length: 450 mm.

Diagnostic characters: Tentacles bear one row of suckers only.

Habitat: Generally distributed, but more frequent in the North; in common with other cephalopods they are not usually seen on shore, but they may be washed up or occasionally seen in rock pools or under stones at extreme low water.

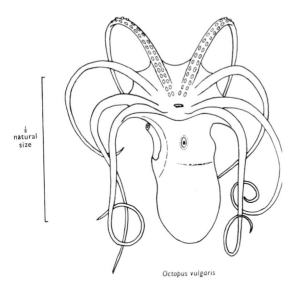

$\frac{1}{8}$ natural size

Octopus vulgaris

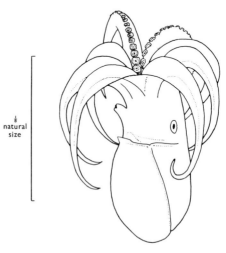

$\frac{1}{8}$ natural size

Eledone cirrhosa

APPENDIX

Glossary of Technical Terms

Accessory plate

Small shell plate additional to the main valves found in the shell of certain bivalves, e.g. the piddocks (*Pholas* and relatives)

Adductor muscles

The main muscles (one or two) joining the two valves of a bivalve shell

Adductor muscle scars

The marks left on the inside of the valves of a bivalve shell by the attachment of the adductor muscles

Aestivation

Period of rest adopted by land pulmonates during periods of adversity, e.g. dry weather

Anus

Posterior terminal opening of the alimentary canal

Anthropophile

Terrestrial gastropod favouring a habitat, e.g. garden, associated with man

Anthropophobe

Terrestrial gastropod avoiding habitats influenced by man

Aperture

The main opening in the shell of a gastropod through which the animal protrudes (referred to in some texts as the 'mouth')

Apex

Uppermost point, or tip, of the gastropod shell

Apophysis

Internal process in the hinge region of certain bivalves, e.g. pholads (rock-boring piddocks)

Beak

Pointed tip of a valve in a bivalve shell, usually regarded as part of the umbo (see below); also jaw in cephalopods

Body whorl

Last (lowermost) and usually largest whorl of gastropod shell

Buccal mass

Muscular anterior part of alimentary canal containing the radula

Byssus

Bundle of tough, horny fibres, composed of tanned protein, used to anchor certain bivalves, e.g. mussels, to the substrate

Calcareous

Consisting of calcium carbonate; limy

Calcicole

Non-marine molluscs requiring limy or calcareous habitats

Calcifuge

Non-marine species avoiding lime

Calciphile

Those favouring limy habitats

Cardinal teeth

(see hinge-teeth)

Cerata

Papilla-like processes borne by the upper body surface of certain sea-slugs

Chondrophore

Pit, below umbo, to which internal ligament is attached in certain bivalves; large, spoon-shaped and protrudes in some forms (e.g. *Mya*, *Lutraria*)

Clausilium

Feature characteristic of most species in a family of land snails, *Clausiliidae*, constituting a protective door-like structure situated in the apertural region of the shell

Columella

Central axis of gastropod shell

Columellar muscle

Muscle attached to the columella, responsible for withdrawing the body of the gastropod into its shell

Ctenidia

Gills

Cuttlebone

Internal shell of a cuttlefish

Decussate

Criss-cross appearance of ridges or grooves on shell surface

Dextral

Shell of a gastropod coiled to the right; with the shell upright, the aperture appears to the right when viewed by the observer

Digestive gland

Blind-ending diverticula of the alimentary canal leading from the stomach, forming gland concerned with the digestion of food particles

Ear

Lateral process of the hinge region of the shell of a scallop

Epiphragm

Dried, often hardened, film of mucus which seals the aperture of certain terrestrial gastropods (pulmonates) during periods of rest (aestivation or hibernation)

Epipodial tentacles

Sensory processes borne laterally by the foot in certain primitive snails

Equilateral

Condition where the valve of a bivalve shell is equally developed anterior and posterior to the umbones

Equivalve

Condition in which the two valves of a bivalve shell are alike

Foot

The main locomotory organ of the mollusc, variously adapted for crawling, burrowing and swimming

Gape

The extent to which the margins of the bivalve shell are apart in the normal living state; can be varied according to the state of contraction of the adductor muscles

Gills

The main respiratory organs, housed in the mantle cavity (respiratory chamber)

Girdle

The muscular, spicular surround of the shell plates in a chiton

Gonad

Reproductive organ, forming male or female germ cells

Growth-lines

Concentric ridges about the umbones on bivalve shells, and spiral striations on shells of gastropods, marking annual, seasonal or shorter periods of growth

Head-scar

Mark left on the inside of a limpet shell by the attachment of the body tissues

Hinge

The upper margin of the shell of a bivalve where the valves meet and are joined together by the ligament; may bear teeth (see below)

Hinge-teeth

Interlocking teeth on the hinge of a bivalve shell, usually centrally placed (cardinal teeth) below the umbones, and lateral, which prevent the valves slipping or shearing on each other

Holobranch

Condition in the chitons in which the gills extend far forward in the groove between mantle and foot

Hygrophile

Terrestrial gastropods which favour wet places

Hypobranchial mucous gland

Main mucus-secreting area in upper part of the mantle cavity

Inequilateral

Condition in which the valves of a bivalve shell show an unequal amount of growth anterior and posterior to the umbones

Inequivalve

Condition in which the valves of a bivalve shell differ in shape and/or structure

Jaw

Hard pad or process of horny material bordering mouth and used in feeding; described as beaks in cephalopods

Keel

Raised ridge

Labial palps

Flap-like structures adjoining the mouth in bivalves and used in the feeding process

Lateral teeth

(see hinge-teeth)

Ligament

Horny, elastic structure in the hinge of a bivalve shell which joins the valves together; may be external, protruding above the hinge-line, or internal, enclosed within the hinge

Lip

The margin of the aperture of a gastropod shell, consisting of outer (peristome) and inner (columellar and parietal) regions

Lung cavity

(see pulmonary cavity)

Lunule

A shallow depression, often heart-shaped, present in some bivalve shells, e.g. venerids, in front of the umbones

Mantle

The thin layer of tissue, also known as the pallium, which covers the visceral mass of a mollusc and secretes the shell; at the margins it also has sensory and muscular properties, and forms the siphon in certain gastropods and many bivalves

Mantle cavity

The important space between the mantle and the foot which acts as a respiratory chamber and primitively houses and protects the gills; it is modified into a lung-like respiratory chamber in air-breathing pulmonate gastropods

Merobranch

Condition in the chitons in which the gills are restricted to the posterior part only of the groove between mantle and foot

Metapodial tentacles

Sensory processes protruding from the rear of the foot in certain gastropods

Mouth

A term which has been applied to the aperture of a univalve shell (see above) but best restricted technically to the anterior opening of the gut

Mucus

Slime

Nacreous layer

Pearly innermost calcareous layer of the shell in many molluscs; replaced in others by different crystalline arrangement

Odontophore

The radula and associated structures constituting the buccal mass

Operculum

Horny or calcareous plug attached to the posterior upper surface of the foot of a snail which seals the aperture of its shell when the animal withdraws

Osphradium

Sense organ in the mantle cavity which samples the incoming respiratory current

Oviduct

Egg-carrying duct in female reproductive system

Pallets

Calcareous plugs sealing the openings of tubes bored in wood by shipworms (*Nototeredo*)

Pallium

Mantle (see above)

Pallial line

Mark left on the inner surface of a bivalve shell by the attachment of the pallial muscles; forms line running near margin of valves between anterior and posterior adductor muscle scars

Pallial muscles

Muscles attaching the mantle edge to the shell in a bivalve

Pallial sinus

Embayment in the pallial line opening towards the posterior end of those bivalves which have appreciable development of the siphons; more marked in those species which have long siphons and are deep burrowers

Parapodia

Lateral flap-like processes of the foot in certain opisthobranch gastropods

Pearl

Sphere of nacreous shell produced around a central nucleus in invaginated sacs within the mantle of certain bivalves

Pedal gland

Mucous gland at anterior end of foot in land gastropods which secretes slime over which the animal can crawl

Pen

Internal reduced horny shell of a squid

Periostracum

Outermost horny organic covering of the shell, composed largely of a hardened, tanned protein

Peristome

(see lip)

Pinnate

Laterally branched, leaf-like

Pneumostome

Opening of pulmonary (lung) chamber in air-breathing gastropods

Prismatic layer

Outer calcareous layer of the shell in many molluscs

Pulmonary cavity

Modified gill-less mantle (respiratory) chamber in air-breathing pulmonate gastropods

Pulmonary opening

(see pneumostome)

Radula

Ribbon-shaped organ bearing teeth, present in buccal mass or odontophore of most gastropods (and also cephalopods, but reduced), used for rasping vegetative matter into small particles for food

Rhinophores

Specialised posterior pair of tentacles borne on the head of opistho-branch gastropods

Rib

Longitudinal raised ridge on whorls of gastropod shell and radiating from umbones in bivalve

Ridge

Spirally arranged striations on gastropod shell and concentric on bivalve (see also growth lines)

Scars

Marks left by muscle or other body attachments on inner surface of mollusc shells (see adductor scar, head-scar, pallial line)

Sculpture

Structural pattern on the shell surface

Shell

The secreted product of the mantle, external in many molluscs but reduced, internal or absent in some

Shell plates

Separate articulating units forming the calcareous shell in the chitons

Sinistral

Shell of a gastropod coiled to the left; with apex uppermost, the aperture appears to the left when viewed by the observer

Siphon

Tubular process of the mantle edge leading into the forward-facing mantle cavity of certain gastropods (e.g. whelks), and comprising the two posteriorly-situated siphons in most bivalves, lower inhalant and upper exhalant

Siphonal canal

Groove in lower edge of aperture of certain gastropod shells (e.g. whelks) through which the siphon (see above) protrudes

Spire

  The whorls of a gastropod shell above the last or body whorl

Striation

  Spirally arranged ridges on surface of a gastropod shell (see also growth-lines)

Suture

  The line formed by the junction between the whorls in a gastropod shell

Synanthropic

  (see anthropophile)

Teeth

  Processes borne by the radula; also used for various processes on the hinge of many bivalves (see hinge-teeth) and in the apertural region of several gastropods

Tentacles

  Sensory processes borne by the head in a gastropod, usually one or two pairs; also applied to various tactile processes of the foot or mantle region

Torsion

  Process by which the visceral hump and shell of a typical gastropod is twisted through a half-circle with respect to the head–foot during development, producing asymmetry in the adult

Tubercle

  Knob-like process of shell or body wall

Umbilicus

  Opening or depression at base of a coiled gastropod (univalve) shell which possesses a hollow columella

Whorl

  A single complete coil of a spirally-wound gastropod shell

Xerophile

  A terrestrial gastropod which prefers dry places

Classification of the Mollusca

Living molluscs, including those British species described in this volume, are classified into groups, the major ones of which, including classes and orders, are listed below. Those requiring a more comprehensive classification of the larger classes down to families are referred to J. E. Morton's 'Molluscs' (Hutchinson University Library) and a complete classified list of the British Mollusca based on publications in the Journal of Conchology is given in 'British Shells' by Nora F. McMillan (Warne).

Class Monoplacophora
  Neopilina the only living representative; no British species
Class Placophora (*Loricata*) (p. 13)
  The chitons
Class Solenogastres (*Aplacophora*)
  Includes certain specialised marine forms, some burrowing and worm-like (e.g. *Chaetoderma*) living in deeper water
Class Gastropoda (p. 16)
  The snails (univalves) and slugs, both aquatic and terrestrial
  Subclass Prosobranchia
    Gastropods with forward-facing respiratory chamber, mainly aquatic
    Order Archaeogastropoda (=*Diotocardia*)
      Most primitive prosobranchs, including the marine limpets and their relatives, trochids (e.g. *Gibbula*), *Tricolia* and the freshwater *Theodoxus*
    Order Mesogastropoda (=*Monotocardia*, in part)
      Largest molluscan order, very successful, including most of the marine snails, ranging from the littorinids (periwinkles) to the cowries, with some freshwater (e.g. *Viviparus*) and, even more limited, terrestrial members (e.g. *Pomatias*)
    Order Neogastropoda (=*Monotocardia*, in part)
      The carnivorous marine whelks and their relatives
  Subclass Opisthobranchia
    Marine gastropods in which the respiratory chamber has moved posteriorly and diminished, and the shell is progressively lost; includes

'*Tectibranchs*'

Actually a number of distinct orders, but all showing some retention of the shell, either external, or more usually, internal and enclosed by the mantle (e.g. *Aplysia*)

Order Nudibranchia

The sea-slugs, naked and lacking a shell

'*Pteropods*'

The planktonic sea-butterflies, comprising two orders, one shelled, the other with naked forms

Subclass Pulmonata

Mainly terrestrial snails and slugs, but with some aquatic representatives

Order Basommatophora

Primitive snails with one pair of tentacles bearing eyes at the base; many are aquatic, e.g. the lymnaeids and planorbids

Order Stylommatophora

Terrestrial snails and slugs, bearing two pairs of tentacles with eyes situated at the tip of the posterior pair

Class Scaphopoda (p. 140)

The marine tusk shells, typified by *Dentalium*

Class Bivalvia (p. 141)

Molluscs with a bivalve shell incorporating a ligament

Subclass Protobranchia

Primitive bivalves, mainly in deeper water (e.g. *Nucula*)

Subclass Lamellibranchia

Includes most bivalves, characterised by a more advanced gill structure. Various classificatory schemes adopting gill, hinge or other structures are in use, none completely satisfactory; the one given here follows that adopted by J. E. Morton

Order Taxodonta

e.g. *Glycymeris*

Order Anisomyaria

Includes many heteromyarian (e.g. *Mytilus*) and monomyarian bivalves (e.g. *Pecten, Ostrea*)

Order Schizodonta

e.g. freshwater mussels (*Unio, Anodonta*)

Order Heterodonta

Includes many common burrowing bivalves, e.g. *Cardiidae*, venerids, tellinids, *Mactra*, also freshwater *Sphaerium* and *Dreissena*

Order Adapedonta

Many deep-burrowing bivalves (e.g. *Ensis*, *Mya*) are included here; also wood and rock-borers (Pholadidae)

Order Anomalodesmata

An advanced group with a variety of habits (e.g. *Thracia*)

Order Septibranchia

Carnivorous bivalves with the gill replaced by a muscular septum, living in deeper water (e.g. *Poromya*, *Cuspidaria*)

Class Cephalopoda (p. 203)

Nautiloids, squids, cuttlefish and octopods, all marine

Subclass Nautiloidea

Includes the tropical *Nautilus*, with an external shell, and many fossil forms

Subclass Ammonoidea

The shelled ammonites, known only as fossils, and common in many geological deposits

Subclass Coleoidea

Cephalopods with a reduced or internal shell, finally lost in the octopods; includes all the British species; major orders are

Order Decapoda

Squids and cuttlefish, with ten arms or tentacles

Order Octopoda

e.g. *Octopus*, with eight tentacles

Addendum

A recently-revised classification of the Mollusca by L. v. Salvini Plawen recognises more explicitly the rather special nature of the chitons and their relatives by proposing the subdivision of the molluscs into two major groupings. One group, the Aculifera, including the Placophora (chitons) and the related Solenogastres, constitutes individuals in which the cuticular portion of the shell bears spiny or spicular processes, and is thereby distinguished from the bulk of molluscs with the more typical shell form, comprising the so-called Conchifera. The latter contains the other main molluscan classes, namely, the Monoplacophora, Gastropoda, Scaphopoda, Bivalvia and Cephalopoda. This distinction underlines the point that the chitons and closely related forms are primitive molluscs (see p. 13), retaining in their shell structure features which may have characterised the ancestors of the molluscan line of evolution.

Collection and preservation of mollusca

Looking for, and collecting molluscs, both as shells and as whole animals, may well stem from a genuine interest in the group as actual living organisms to see how they live and function in, and are related to, their natural environment, i.e. their ecology, as much as from a desire to acquire specimens. In either case, the would-be collector needs to be aware of the best possible sites within the multitude of marine, fresh-water and terrestrial habitats where molluscs can be found, and should be encouraged to keep accurate records of the specimens collected.

Collecting specimens

The seashore is a rich source of material for the collector of marine molluscs. The shore or littoral zone extends technically from high-water to low-water mark but the actual range of this intertidal area is determined by the tidal flow. This varies from the low range neap tides to the extensive spring tides, which occur fortnightly during the periods of new and full moon. Following C. M. Yonge, one can divide the shore into three general zones, the upper shore, covered only by tides of above-average range passing from neap to spring tides; the middle shore, encompassing the average tidal range and inhabited by the most typical seashore species; and finally, the lower shore, only exposed by the above-average tides, down to the lowermost limit of the spring tides. This latter zone is the one in which the collector stands the best chance of seeing the widest range of molluscs, and indeed of all sea-shore animals, moving down towards low-water mark during the last hour or two as the spring tide ebbs, uncovering the *Laminaria* zone. The spring tides themselves also vary in range, being at their greatest during the March and September equinoxes, when field courses for marine students and collectors tend to be arranged and collecting is at its most fruitful. Here in the richly inhabited lower shore, molluscs may be found which are normally completely covered by water and are often representative of species inhabiting the truly marine environment off-shore in the so-called sub-littoral zone. The boundary between the lowermost part of the shore and deeper water is marked by the tall brown fronds of the characteristic seaweed *Laminaria*. In this region might be found many nudibranchs, especially in the spring when these seaslugs approach the shore to breed and lay their often characteristic jelly-like egg-masses. The fronds, stem and holdfast of the *Laminaria* itself should be searched for its own special fauna, including the limpet *Patina* and several other molluscs.

Even without the spring tides the typical rocky shore reveals many molluscs to the careful observer. In addition to the obvious limpets and mussels attached to rock surfaces, the littorinids (periwinkles), top shells and dog whelks usually ubiquitous on the shore, many molluscs can be found in damp, sheltered habitats, including cracks and crevices, overhanging rock surfaces, under and amongst weeds, under stones and rocks (after turning these over to collect shells, remember to replace the rock right-side up in its original position) and in rock pools, which represent an ideal habitat for those littoral animals which cannot tolerate exposure. Collecting representative samples of weed from rock surfaces or pools to search at leisure later may reveal many molluscs, especially smaller snails, not immediately apparent. The region above high water, the so-called splash zone which is only wetted by the spray is also worth exploring, especially in cracks and crevices for its own specialised fauna, including the small periwinkle, which favour this drier exposed environment. Examination of the rocks themselves may reveal the openings and channels made by boring molluscs, especially in softer rocks, e.g. limestone, and in stiff, hardened clay; carefully breaking these open with a small hammer and chisel will enable the animals to be recovered whole.

The apparent paucity of molluscan life in sandy and muddy shores is usually misleading. In addition to the often interesting shells found washed up on the surface, and the specimens attached to scattered rocks and boulders or on wooden piles and breakwaters, all more characteristic of the rocky shore environment, a great many interesting molluscs, especially bivalves, live buried in their natural environment within the substrate. Some may be washed ashore on the surface after strong onshore weather but most can only be obtained by digging. Forking in sand at low water will expose many common bivalves, including the tellins, venerids, cockles, and if rapid enough, the razor shells (a sprinkle of salt on the surface may help to catch these). In muddier substrates will be found the gapers (*Mya*), otter shells (*Lutraria*) and *Scrobicularia*, all deep burrowers with long siphons. The apparently unappetising mud surface of estuaries may abound in the tiny snail, *Hydrobia*.

Searching for molluscs in freshwater habitats embodies the same principles as indeed in all habitats: patience, a good eye and examining

under and beneath suitable substrates, including vegetation, rather than
the obvious surface areas. Slow-moving, but not stagnant and polluted,
waters are often the most rewarding, particularly those with a reasonable
lime content. Sweeping the shallow waters with nets and collecting
vegetation to search later can be effective techniques. Canals, rich but
not choked with weeds, are likely sources of material since they represent an amalgam of ideal conditions for freshwater molluscs. Even ponds
can be useful, despite the unfortunate fact that they, like many natural
marshy areas, tend to be dwindling both in size and number. Some of
the really classic studies on British freshwater molluscs have been
conducted on pond faunas. Least productive are swift-flowing waters,
except of course for certain species such as the pearl-mussel *Margaritifera* and the river limpet *Ancylus* specially adapted to life in these
conditions, and lakes with very soft or acid peaty waters.

For terrestrial gastropods, the combination of calcareous (limy) soils
and suitable shelter and moisture often produce the most productive
areas for collecting land snails. Under fallen leaves, especially in beech
woods, in and under rotting logs, in crevices or under stones, all tend
to be rich sources of material. Other valuable collecting grounds, however, many with their own special characteristics, include grassy
downlands, hedgerows and waysides, amongst herbage and litter,
derelict areas, sand-dunes and coastal areas, old gardens, and a whole
range of more specialised habitats ranging from practically aquatic
localities to crevices in walls, churchyards and tree trunks.

Whatever the source of their collection, perhaps the most crucial
exercise is the documentation of the shells and specimens found. This
involves accurately recording, at the time, provisional identification
(this can be checked later), nature of the habitat, locality, including the
county, the National Grid reference obtainable from an ordnance
survey map, nature of the specimen (e.g. alive, dead shell), date, the
collector's name, and any other relevant notes. When the identification
and record is completed the information may be very valuable in help-
ing to map the distribution of molluscs in the British Isles. At present
the Conchological Society is engaged in re-mapping the location of land
and freshwater molluscs on a 10-kilometre grid system successfully
used earlier by botanists to map the distribution of British plants. It is
hoped thereby to portray more accurately the changing distribution of
molluscs in the British Isles, at present shown by the 1951 Census,
also conducted by the Conchological Society, based on the vice-

county system. The Census Recorder (currently Dr. M. P. Kerney, Department of Geology, Imperial College, Prince Consort Rd., London, S.W.7) will be pleased to supply Record Cards and further information on the distribution mapping scheme. The Conchological Society is also pioneering a census of marine molluscs (present Marine Recorder: Stella M. Turk—for details see paper by this author in reading list) to which the beginner who accurately documents his records can expect to make a useful contribution.

How to Collect

The actual collecting of molluscs in the field requires little specialised equipment. For general purposes, suitable polythene-capped tubes or polythene bags will be of value for holding the specimens, as well as screw-top jars for the larger specimens. A knife for prising limpets and chitons off rocks will also be useful, as well as forceps for picking up small species, a notebook and soft pencil for recording habitats and other data, and labels. A pocket lens is also desirable. As previously indicated, a hammer and chisel will be needed for extracting rock-borers. On sandy and muddy beaches a strong garden fork will be needed for digging, along with a supply of sieves for separating smaller specimens from the substrate. Strong hand nets of nylon or muslin are useful for sweeping rock pools and freshwater habitats amongst weed or other vegetation. Although collecting specimens off-shore may be beyond most beginners it is quite easy to tow simple nets from a small boat to sample the microscopic life in the surface waters, which may contain planktonic molluscs or larval forms. Dredging the sea bed in shallow water is also feasible where a suitable dredge might be hired and approaches to sympathetic local fishermen might provide access to off-shore molluscs taken which are not required for food or are super-fluous to their requirements. Collectors should be encouraged to take back to the bench samples of vegetation, weed for freshwater and marine species and humus and fallen leaves for terrestrial molluscs, to sample later at leisure for the smaller shells.

After collection, material should be examined live where possible (if aquatic in water equivalent to that in its natural environment), especially in those cases where the features of the living animal are necessary for identification. In the soft-bodied molluscs, of course, including the terrestrial slugs, marine nudibranchs, and where available, the cephalopods, this is the only satisfactory way to ascertain their identity, the subsequently preserved specimen being a poor substitute. Similarly, observations on the living animal may lead to ecological (environmental) and physiological studies and experiments which could further knowledge as to the functional morphology of the mollusc and its relationship to the environment; both approaches which should be encouraged. Keeping specimens alive, in fact, is not necessarily difficult. Freshwater snails and small mussels, especially those which favour or tolerate static waters, can be kept relatively easily in a small balanced aquarium, containing suitable pond weed (e.g. *Elodea*), which need not therefore be artificially aerated. The large freshwater mussels, *Unio* and *Anodonta*, are not so easy to maintain in such conditions; they soon die and pollute the water. If required for longer periods alive they will survive for some time in running water in tanks kept outside. Keeping a seawater aquarium poses greater problems because marine molluscs, like most animals that live in the sea, are less tolerant of confined spaces. The water needs to be kept cool and weed should not be included. With careful choice of specimens (not too large) and some artificial aeration there is no reason why a marine aquarium should not be feasible. Terrestrial snails and slugs can be kept, at least for some time, in a vivarium or terrarium constructed of a suitable container (e.g. a gauze-sided box) containing the same material which constitutes the mollusc's natural environment. A sloping layer of soil over stones, covered with moss, leaves, sticks and humus provides necessary shelter and moisture. The vivarium should be kept moist and cleaned regularly. The species maintained should be allowed adequate space, the larger the specimen the greater its spatial requirement. The slugs and snails have to be fed regularly rather than trying to provide a permanent vegetative food source. Lettuce, dandelion, sliced root vegetables, bran, plus some lime are acceptable, with a wide range of other 'titbits' which vary according to the species.

Preservation
If the mollusc is not required for observations on the living animal it needs to be killed and preserved. Ideally, two specimens should be kept, one for the dried shell, the other for the body tissues in a suitable preserving fluid. For the latter, the animal needs first to be relaxed by anaesthetization or narcotization. With marine species this can be achieved by adding small quantities of magnesium sulphate to the water at regular intervals until the animals are fully extended and relaxed.

Such treatment unfortunately tends to make the tissues unsuitable for future detailed cytological work; for such requirements professional biologists sometimes use propylene phenoxetol (to 1% solution), which is a good relaxant and at the same time less damaging to the tissues. Terrestrial snails and slugs and freshwater molluscs can be narcotized in firmly stoppered bottles or jars completely filled with water which has been previously boiled to lower its oxygen content and subsequently cooled. The animals are asphyxiated in approximately 24 hours. If time is short the slugs and snails may be plunged whilst in an extended state into boiling water for a few minutes. Preservation of the body is then accomplished by transferring the narcotized animal to a suitable fixative, usually 70–90% alcohol (industrial, not methylated, and preferably via a weaker 50% solution to prevent shrinkage) or 5% formalin (one part of concentrated 40% formaldehyde to 19 parts of water, fresh or salt depending on the animal's natural environment). The formalin should be buffered or neutralised with borax, calcium carbonate or hexamine to prevent dissolution of the shell and other calcareous material. Chitons should be preserved whilst gently pressed between two slides or other flat surfaces to prevent them curling up. Specimens can subsequently be stored in buffered formalin or alcohol, preferably after changing the fluid. For long-term storage alcohol shows less tendency to cause shrinkage. For detailed histological study of the animal's tissues special fixatives, e.g. Bouin's fluid, may be required; for particulars of these, a suitable histology textbook should be consulted.

Where only the shell is required, the animal can be killed in boiling water, in the case of land and freshwater species, or, for marine molluscs, allowing them to die in stale seawater, and then in all cases carefully extracting the soft parts from the shell. Care should be taken to retain the operculum where it occurs in gastropod shells. This can then be replaced in the aperture, which in life it guards, gummed to a piece of cotton wool to hold it in position in the empty shell. The shell, now denuded of the animal, or if it was originally collected in the empty state, can then be gently washed and cleaned with a soft brush, avoiding damage to the outer horny periostracum, and then allowing it to dry naturally. Shells should never be subsequently 'touched up,' varnished or otherwise treated to simulate or enhance natural characteristics. Bivalve shells which gape when dead due to the opening thrust of the elastic ligament, may be allowed to dry with the valves closed together and tied with thread or nylon cord. If the valves have been separated to view the hinge structure and the ligament cut, the valves may still be similarly united to avoid one or other being misplaced.

Starting a Collection

Specimens, whether dried shells or preserved specimens, can now be arranged to form a collection. The confirmed identification of the species, with a brief summary of the other information made during collecting should be written clearly, preferably in black Indian ink on a small specimen label kept inside the same container as the specimen. This should comprise a corked glass tube for smaller shells or a glass-topped box for larger specimens. Sealed polythene bags can also be used for the latter. Each specimen can be numbered and catalogued separately thereby keeping an overall check on the collection. The specimen containers could then be housed in a suitable partitioned drawer, or if available, a display cabinet, as the collection builds up. Preserved specimens, similarly labelled, should be kept separately in their own screw- or glass-topped containers, the fluid being kept topped up to counteract evaporation. A good collection is reflected by the accuracy of the information which accompanies it.

Societies

Those interested in the study of molluscs are encouraged to subscribe to and make use of the publications and scientific meetings of the two British Societies specializing in this field. These are:—

The Malacological Society of London, Hon. Secretary: Dr. J. E. Rigby, Department of Biology, Queen Elizabeth College, Campden Hill Road, London, W.8.

The Conchological Society of Great Britain and Northern Ireland, Hon. Secretary: Mr. T. E. Crowley, B.Sc., The Cottage, Church Street, Bampton, Oxon.

Suggested further reading

The following provide much useful additional information for detailed identification of molluscan species:

Barrett, J. H., and Yonge, C. M., 1958. *Collins Pocket Guide to the Seashore*. Collins, London.

Includes comprehensive sections on the marine Mollusca.

Cloudsley-Thompson, J. L., and Sankey, J., 1961. *Land Invertebrates: A Guide to British Worms, Molluscs and Arthropods (excluding Insects)*. Methuen, London.

Incorporates useful section, including key, on molluscs.

Eales, N. B., 1961. *The Littoral Fauna of the British Isles: A Handbook for Collectors*. 3rd Edn. Cambridge University Press.

A detailed guide to the shore molluscs, as well as other marine groups; particularly useful for advanced students.

Ellis, A. E., 1926. *British Snails*. Oxford University Press (reprinted 1969).

A standard guide to British non-marine gastropods; most readable and comprehensive.

Ellis, A. E., 1962. *British Freshwater Bivalve Molluscs: Synopses of the British Fauna* No. 13. Linnean Society. (Obtainable through the Secretary of the Linnean Society, Burlington House, Piccadilly, London, W.1.)

A definitive work dealing with all species, including those of the 'difficult' *Pisidium*.

Ellis, A. E., 1964. *Key to Land Shells of Great Britain*. Conchological Society: Papers for students No. 3. (These and other papers in the series are obtainable through the Hon. Sec. Conchological Society, The Cottage, Church Street, Bampton, Oxfordshire.)

Ellis, A. E., 1969. *Key to British Slugs*. Papers for Students No. 12. Published by the Conchological Society.

Graham, A., 1971. *British Prosobranch and other Operculate Gastropod Molluscs*. Synopses of British Fauna (New Series) No. 2. Publ. for Linn. Soc. by Acad. Press.

James, B. L., 1968. *The Distribution and Keys of Species in the Family Littorinidae and of their Digenean Parasites in the Region of Dale Pemb*. Field Studies Vo. 2, No. 5. (For source see Morton et al below.)

Janus, H., 1965. *The Young Specialist looks at Land and Freshwater Molluscs*. Burke, London.

Covers all the British species of land and freshwater molluscs, incorporating many keys and useful diagrams.

Macan, T. T., 1960. *A Key to the British Fresh- and Brackish-Water Gastropods* with notes on their ecology. Scientific Publications No. 13 of the Freshwater Biological Association. (Copies obtainable from The Ferry House, Far Sawrey, Ambleside, Westmorland.)
Well illustrated and comprehensive.

Matthews, Gillian, 1967. *The Identification of British Chitons*. Papers for students No. 9. Published by The Conchological Society.

McMillan, Nora F., 1968. *British Shells*. Wayside and Woodland Series. Warne, London, New York.
Nicely produced guide to practically all native molluscs; replaces Edward Step's *Shell Life*, published originally in 1901 in the same series.

Morton, J. E., and Machin, J., 1959. *A Key to the Land Snails of the Flatford Area, Suffolk*. Field Studies, Vol. 1, No. 1. (Copies available through The Field Studies Council, 9 Devereux Court, Strand, London, W.C.2.)
Neat well-illustrated guide with a useful key.

Quick, H. E., 1949. *Slugs: Synopses of the British Fauna*, No. 8. Linnean Society (see above).
A readable guide to British slugs.

Quick, H. E., 1960. *British Slugs (Pulmonata, Testacellidae, Arionidae, Limacidae). Bulletin of the British Museum (Natural History)*, Zoology, Vol. 6., No. 3.
A more detailed account of the British species.

Tebble, N., 1966. *British Bivalve Seashells; A Handbook for Identification*. Brit. Mus. (Nat. Hist.), London.
Very comprehensive guide to marine bivalves, with many keys, descriptions and diagrams; well illustrated.

Turk, Stella M., 1966. *Collecting Shells*. Foyles Handbooks, London.
Very useful introduction to the beginner with valuable hints on collecting.

Turk, Stella M., 1969. *Collecting British Marine Molluscs*. Papers for Students No. 11. Published by The Conchological Society.

For more detailed reading, including standard literature and references to original work on the Mollusca, the following should be consulted:

Alder, J., and Hancock, A., 1845–1855. *A Monograph of the British Nudibranchiate Mollusca*. Ray Society, 7 parts. Supplementary Part 8 by Eliot, C., 1919. Ray Society.

Boycott, A. E., 1934. The habitats of land Mollusca in Britain. *J. Ecol.*, **22**, 1–38.

Boycott, A. E., 1936. The habitats of freshwater Mollusca in Britain. *J. anim. Ecol.*, **5**, 116–186.

These remain the two standard and classic accounts of the way of life of non-marine molluscs in the British Isles.

Cooke, A. H., 1895. *Molluscs and Brachiopods*. Cambr. Nat. Hist. Vol. 3.

Ellis, A. E., 1951. Census of the distribution of British non-marine Mollusca. *J. Conch.*, **23**, 171–244.

Forbes, E., and Hanley, S., 1849–1853. *A History of British Mollusca and their Shells*. 4 vols., London.

Fretter, V., and Graham, A., 1962. *British Prosobranch Molluscs: Their Functional Anatomy and Ecology*. Ray Society, London.

A must for the discerning students of these primitive gastropods with a wealth of information for the naturalist as well as those interested in comparative anatomy.

Hyman, L. H., 1967. *The Invertebrates: Volume VI Mollusca I*. McGraw-Hill.

Part of a classic review of the invertebrates, this volume deals with primitive molluscan groups, including the chitons, and the Gastropoda.

Jeffreys, J. G., 1862–1869. *British Conchology*. 5 Vols. London.

Kew, H. W., 1893. *The Dispersal of Shells*. London.

Morton, J. E., 1967. *Molluscs*. 4th Revised Edn. Hutchinson University Library, London.

A very valuable book on all aspects of the Mollusca.

Purchon, R. D., 1969. *The Biology of the Mollusca*. Pergamon.

Sowerby, G. B., 1859. *Illustrated Index of British Shells*. London.

Taylor, J. W., 1894–1921. *Monograph of the Land and Freshwater Mollusca of the British Isles*. 3 Vols. and 3 parts of 4th Vol. (unfinished).

Not completed but a monumental and standard work.

Wilbur, K. M., and Yonge, C. M. (editors), 1964, 1966. *Physiology of Mollusca* Vols. I and II. Academic Press.

Valuable reviews of advanced work on topics of ecological as well as physiological interest.

Winckworth, R., 1932. The British Marine Mollusca. *J. Conch.*, **19**, 217–250.

Winckworth, R., 1951. A list of the marine Mollusca of the British Isles: Additions and corrections. *J. Conch.*, **23**, 131–4.

Yonge, C. M., 1960. *Oysters*. New Naturalist Series: Special Volume. Collins, London.

There are also in addition several general books which include useful and informative accounts of various aspects of the life of the Mollusca.

Cain, A. J., 1963. *Animal Species and their Evolution* (Revd. Edn.) Hutchinson University Library, London.

   Introduction to taxonomy and classification with some useful references to the land snails, *Cepaea*.

Clegg, J., 1965. *The Freshwater Life of the British Isles*. 3rd Edn. Warne, London.

Ellis, E. A., 1965. *The Broads*. New Naturalist Series. Collins, London.

Evans, I. O. (editor) 1962. *The Observer's Book of Sea and Seashore*. Warne, London.

Hardy, A. C., 1956. *The Open Sea: I. The World of Plankton*. New Naturalist Series. Collins, London.

Hardy, A. C., 1959. *The Open Sea: II. Fish and Fisheries*. New Naturalist Series. Collins, London.

   Contains much useful information on the molluscan fauna of the sea-bed.

Lewis, J. R., 1964. *The Ecology of Rocky Shores*. English Universities Press, London.

Macan, T. T., and Worthington, E. B., 1951. *Life in Lakes and Rivers*. New Naturalist Series. Collins, London.

Sankey, J., 1966. *Chalkland Ecology*. Heinemann, London.

Sheppard, P. M., 1967. *Natural Selection and Heredity*. 3rd Edn. Hutchinson University Library.

   Incorporates a useful account of polymorphism and genetic variation in the land snail, *Cepaea*.

Southward, A. J., 1965. *Life on the Seashore*. Heinemann, London.

Yonge, C. M., 1949. *The Sea Shore*. New Naturalist Series. Collins, London.

   One of the most readable accounts of seashore life, with a wealth of information on the Mollusca.

INDEX

Note: Figures in bold italics represent main descriptive reference with an illustration on the facing page.

Notes